Beyond the HST

A proposed design strategy
for future trains in Britain

John Kinghorn

Cover Image: *The 125 mph diesel InterCity 125 High Speed Train (HST) has served the British railway network well for the last third of a century. This one disappears into Box tunnel on a Bristol to London service. What kind of train should replace it?*

Published by

**MELROSE
BOOKS**

An Imprint of Melrose Press Limited
St Thomas Place, Ely
Cambridgeshire
CB7 4GG, UK
www.melrosebooks.com

FIRST EDITION

ISBN 978-1-907040-65-8

Printed and bound in Malta by:
Latitude Press Ltd.

Plate 1: *The InterCity 125 High Speed Train (HST) was first introduced on the Great Western main lines in 1976, bringing new standards of speed and comfort to long distance rail travel in Britain. These three HSTs seen at London Paddington 33 years later are still providing services to Penzance, Swansea and Bristol. It is now time to consider what the next generation of trains should be, with the objectives of improving comfort, speed, accessibility, flexibility and energy efficiency for the mid 21st century.*

Plate 2: *New high speed lines have a major role to play in Britain as elsewhere in Europe, but they can only be justified commercially where routes have high traffic levels. Two Eurostar trains, capable of 186 mph, are being prepared at London St Pancras International for services to Paris and Brussels.*

Preface

I have been interested in trains for as long as I can remember. As a child growing up in the 1950s, the exploits of *Thomas the Tank Engine* helped my first faltering steps in the art of reading. The real railway then meant trips to the seaside at Whitley Bay on 1930s articulated electric trains, or travelling to exotic locations like Edinburgh behind exciting steam engines with romantic names like Quicksilver or Blink Bonny.

Twenty-five years later found me working in south London, where the slam-door suburban trains seemed very archaic although efficient at their task. Long-distance journeys, however, were now dramatically improved. Fast and comfortable electric or diesel trains covered most routes under the InterCity branding, with the new 125mph High Speed Trains (HSTs) providing world-leading levels of speed and frequency.

Moving onward a further quarter-century to the present day, some splendid things have happened on the railways with the opening of the Channel Tunnel and new high speed lines linking it to the magnificent St Pancras terminus. Not surprisingly, these new international services have a high market share.

On the domestic rail network, however, the maximum speed remains 125mph, although new trains for both the East and West Coast main lines were designed for 140mph. As far as passenger comfort is concerned, no newer train design surpasses the HSTs for spaciousness, quietness and smoothness of ride, and many are significantly worse in these aspects.

Now living on the south coast, I can travel to London on a 'fast' electric train which gives a somewhat less bumpy ride than twenty-five years ago, but still cannot be described as smooth. It also takes almost the same time as it did then, with a maximum speed of 100mph and an average of 58mph. This kind of story is repeated throughout the country. Away from the favoured main lines, few journeys are much faster than they were in the 1980s. Some are slower.

Sometimes I take a cross-country journey back to my Tyneside roots, on an often overcrowded diesel electric multiple unit train which generates added noise and vibration to inhibit dozing. It travels at a maximum speed of 125mph but has an average of only 55mph for my long journey. That is the average for the rail miles travelled, not in a direct line; the average speed drops to 43mph for the real distance as the crow flies, not that crows travel that way often. Is this an adequate level of service for our crowded island in the 21st Century? I doubt it.

In a few years time the HSTs will be forty years old and coming to the end of their lives, so what will replace them? One contender is the SET (Super Express Train) promoted by the Department for Transport (DfT). From the passenger's point of view this has the depressingly familiar 'distributed power' train concept with all its problems of rough ride, noise and vibration, together with a long 26m coach body to squeeze in more passengers per toilet and per door. It also has the now standard minimalist seating in mostly 'airline' style. In other words, the SET is significantly worse than the HST for passenger comfort.

An alternative proposal promoted by several commentators is a conventional 125mph locomotive-hauled train based on standard European designs. This is potentially much better than an SET, but is not very innovative: it can equal an HST for comfort and performance, but not surpass it significantly.

Since the new trains, whatever they are, will last forty years, they will still be around in 2060 (although I shall not). What kind of society and travel expectations will there be in Britain then? Will they really be satisfied with 1980s levels of speed and comfort? That is what will happen at best if either of these train design strategies is followed. In other words, there will be eighty years of no significant improvement. Would you accept 1930s standards of train performance now? I thought not.

Of course in theory it is possible to build lots of new dedicated high speed rail lines to transform performance, but realistically how many can be afforded and how long will it take to build them? The majority of locations in Britain will remain dependent on the existing rail network and its trains for many years to come. That means a lot of unlucky places unless train design can be improved.

It was while thinking these gloomy thoughts in Grumpy Old Cynic mode that a little voice at the back of my head said, "All right, clever clogs, it is easy to criticise. What would YOU do as a better alternative for trains on the established British network?"

That seemed a fair question. I thought the main issues were to go faster than the 125mph established thirty years ago, to improve the comfort and spaciousness of the passenger environment, and to ease accessibility by more even door spacing and having coach floors level with platforms. It would also be desirable to have the flexibility to alter train formations freely in traffic, and to give due attention to energy-saving possibilities for better environmental credentials and lower running costs. A wider applicability of the components to cover different kinds of trains, and sensible re-use of existing assets, would be bonuses. The needs of passengers, train operators and infrastructure providers would be appropriately balanced, within the context of a stable regulatory environment designed to encourage the railway network to carry a greater share of the transport needs of the country. Above all, it would be achievable at a reasonable cost with established technologies pushed to sensible limits, using neither gold-plated-techie-heaven-overkill nor buy-cheap-now-and-regret-it-later philosophies.

"That sounds a reasonable set of objectives," said the little voice. "But how do you achieve them? The devil is in the detail, you know."

So I set out to study some possibilities, and in time they fell together into what seemed to be a sensible overall design strategy. It looked rather good in fact; I was getting enthusiastic.

Back came the little voice again. "That seems a fair strategy. But you have never been a railway professional, and your background in electronic systems engineering means that your mechanical engineering knowledge is limited. Better check out the ideas with a proper mechanical engineer to see whether they are sensible before proceeding further."

So I did. Initial indications are that the concepts do seem to be viable, although much more work needs to be done to produce detailed designs and find optimum solutions to the various issues that will arise.

Consequently, here follows one man's vision of what could be done for the design of future trains on the existing British railway network. It does not cover the trains for dedicated new high speed lines going at 180mph or more, nor does it include short-distance metro-type trains either. However, there are ideas for almost every sort of passenger train between these two extremes, using standard vehicles that can be freely coupled together in many ways to cover a large variety of requirements. I hope you find it interesting.

My grateful thanks go to Dr Julian Dunne of the University of Sussex for checking the mechanical engineering aspects of the concept in relation to train dynamics.

John Kinghorn
January 2010

Author's Note

Since this book was written there has been a general election and a change of government, with a new emphasis on cutting expenditure to reduce the budget deficit. So far, however, railway investment projects have come out of the Comprehensive Spending Review process quite well.

The major London projects of Crossrail and the Thameslink upgrade will continue, with orders for new rolling stock expected soon. This will release many existing electric trains for improvement of services elsewhere.

Electrification of lines in Lancashire between Liverpool, Manchester, Preston and Blackpool has been confirmed, giving new opportunities for long distance electric trains as well as a great improvement in local services. The 'outer suburban' area of the Great Western is also to be electrified, covering the lines from London to Reading, Newbury, Didcot and Oxford. Critics might ask for more, sooner, but this new situation is a vast improvement on the 'policy' of a few years ago which paralysed progress on electrification for two decades.

Regarding HST replacement, the government has now ruled out refurbishment of the InterCity 125s as a solution for the future. It has also ruled out the idea of forcing passengers to change trains from electric to diesel where the wires end: through trains will continue. The question of what those through trains should be is still undecided. Two options are currently officially under consideration.

In the first option, the big mistake of the original bi-mode SET design (inadequate power in diesel mode) has now been recognised, and a revised approach is being developed using underfloor diesel engines. This seems like a long convoluted way of ending up with another mediocre diesel electric multiple unit having an overhead electric power option. If that is all that is wanted, a much easier way is to add a pantograph and transformer car to a Voyager or Meridian; a solution some are now advocating for the Midland main line to allow an incremental electrification approach there.

A second new alternative solution is an 'all-electric train' (presumably a multiple unit) hauled by a new diesel locomotive where electrification ceases. This is a bit better, but has the usual multiple unit inflexibility and other issues.

The author is still convinced that the solution proposed in the following pages is a much better idea than either of these alternatives. Read on, dear reader, and decide for yourself.....

29th November 2010

Contents

Chapter 1

The network

Although this book is primarily about train design, it is necessary to consider how trains and the network interact as a complete system. Each will influence the other, and more broadly both will be influenced by the commercial, political and regulatory environment in which they exist.

This proposal assumes that the context is an enlightened government policy which has the objective to increase steadily rail's market share of domestic travel for environmental, economic and social reasons. This broad objective has cross-party support and does not change significantly for decades. A modest growth is desired, with sustained capital expenditure over a long term, allowing proper strategic planning and building up skills in stable, well-managed teams. The governance structure of the railway industry is stable, effective and accepted by all participants. Policies and regulatory issues are the domain of civil servants, but management of the industry as a whole is left to railway professionals in a collaborative environment.

Given such a foundation, it seems reasonable to suppose that the passenger railway network would expand a little from its current size over the next quarter-century, but not dramatically. Some new dedicated high speed lines would be constructed, but they are outside the scope of this book. New lines in the main national network would be primarily re-openings of Victorian era routes, mostly to connect significant areas of commuter housing to provincial cities. There would be a few lines on new alignments to improve speeds, facilitate new flows or ease congestion, together with the major London project of Crossrail. Overall passenger route mileage would be about 5% greater in 2035 than it is now.

Figure 1 shows the passenger railway network as it is at present. There has been a small expansion in the last quarter-century: lines for passenger services introduced since 1985 are shown in red.

By 2035 the network might look something like *Figure 2*; new passenger lines are shown in purple. Many of these have been discussed or planned already and a few

1

Plate 3: *The British railway network has been quite stable in size since the 1970s, after the devastating closures of the Beeching era in the 1960s. A few new lines and stations have been opened in recent years, successfully bringing new business to the railways. This is the station at Alloa, serving a population of 19,000, which opened in 2008. The new service attracted about 400,000 passengers in its first year, more than double the forecast.*

are under construction. Some other suggestions have been added for new routes which might stand a reasonable chance of being built in that timescale.

Regarding the motive power, the proposal assumes that no new alternative technologies will become available in the next few years and the practical options will remain electric or diesel (possibly bio-diesel) traction. The electrified routes of the present network are shown in orange in *Figure 3*.

At present, Britain remains well down the list of developed nations for the percentage of route mileage that is electrified. Although the benefits of electrification are well known, inexplicably decision-makers fought against its expansion for many years. Fortunately there is evidence of more enlightened attitudes recently, and there are grounds for hope that a sensible long-term rolling programme of electrification will be announced soon. It is assumed that a positive decision will be taken here, and the Midland, Great Western and Cross Country routes will be given priority, together

Plate 4: *Some new stations have even been opened to serve small communities. This is Beauly, west of Inverness on the routes to Kyle of Lochalsh, Wick and Thurso. It opened in 2002 to serve a village of 1,200 inhabitants, a simple short platform and shelter being sufficient to provide a valued local service.*

with some obvious missing links.[1] The electrified network would then look something like *Figure 4* by 2025 or so, the newly-electrified lines being shown in pink with the existing ones in orange.

At this date there would still be many through trains travelling on partly electrified routes, but they would change between electric and diesel traction at the boundaries to avoid diesel haulage in electrified areas for environmental, performance and efficiency reasons.

Since the overall system benefits of electrification become greater as the electrified network increases in size, it is assumed that the same level of electrification resources will continue to be deployed and not disbanded after the above routes are complete. This would result in all the medium and high density traffic corridors being electrically worked by 2035. *Figure 5* estimates the situation then with the additional electrified

---

1   Since writing this chapter in summer 2009, electrification of the Great Western lines from London as far as Swansea, Bristol, Oxford and Newbury has been approved, together with the original Liverpool to Manchester main line and both Manchester and Liverpool to Preston and Blackpool. Excellent news!

lines in pink. On the former Southern Region, electrification would be complete and diesel operation of passenger trains there would be eliminated entirely.

This steady programme of modest route expansion, together with a transformation into a mostly electrified system, would produce a substantially better passenger rail

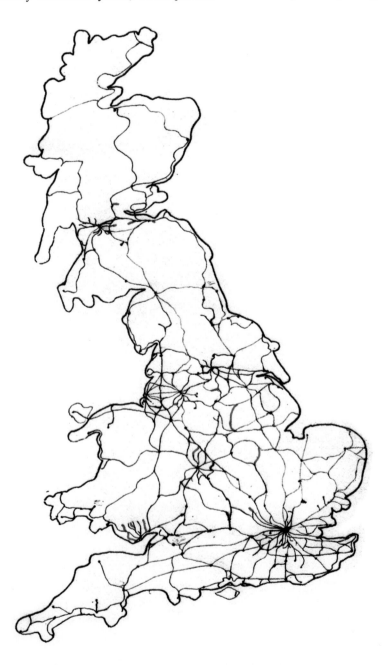

Figure 1: *Passenger rail network 2009. New services since 1985 in red.*

network by 2035. With the appropriate train services, to be described later, it would facilitate more even economic development and social benefits throughout the country, with less disparity between favoured main lines and neglected secondary routes.

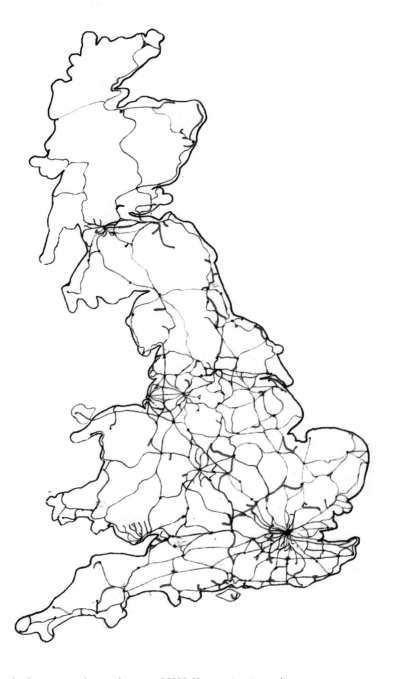

Figure 2: *Passenger rail network proposed 2035. New services in purple.*

Although outside the scope of this book, network infrastructure improvements for the benefit of freight services would also take place over the same period. These would be focused mainly on loading gauge enhancement for larger containers on standard wagons, electrification of core freight routes, and some new lines to alleviate

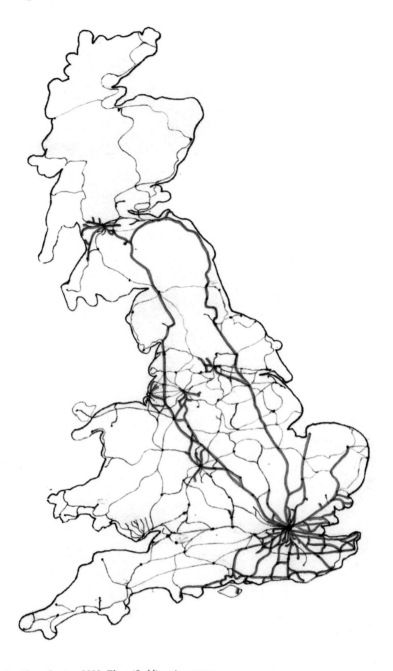

Figure 3: *Electrification 2009. Electrified lines in orange.*

congestion. Particular needs include strong links from Thames Haven and Felixstowe to the Midlands and North avoiding London, alternative routes to avoid congested main lines, and enhanced facilities for ports such as Teesport. Some of these freight enhancements have good synergy with passenger improvements: for example, electrification

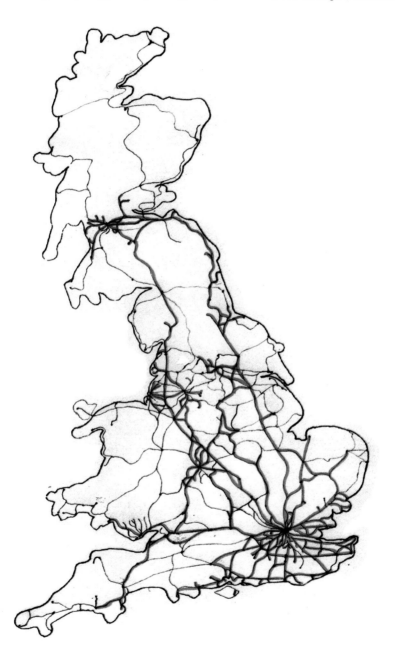

Figure 4: *Electrification 2025. New electrified lines in pink.*

from Ely to Peterborough primarily for freight would also provide an electrified diversionary East Coast passenger route and facilitate direct services from Stansted Airport to Leeds.

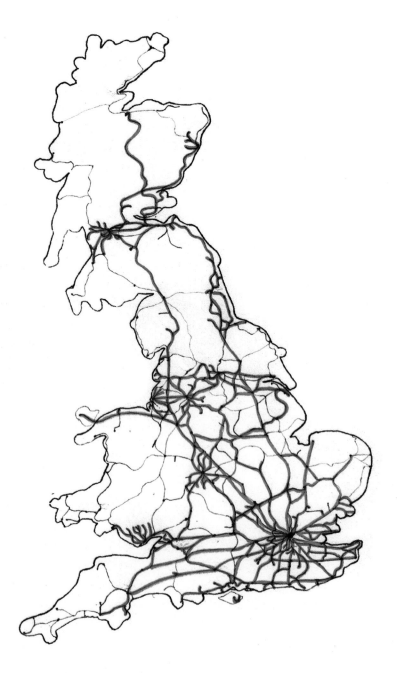

Figure 5: *Electrification 2035. New electrified lines in pink.*

Chapter 2

Going faster

One of the objectives of the proposed strategy is to speed up journeys on the network overall. Shorter journey times have many benefits: they will attract more passengers, they will increase revenue, and fewer trains will be needed for the same frequency of service. A generally faster pace on the whole network increases the usefulness of the rail system to those making journeys to or from smaller places as well as big cities.

Good connections are important in this context: it is little help to have a fast train to an intermediate point if completing the journey then means a long wait for another train to the final destination. There should be a reasonable expectation of consistent standards on the network as a whole, in contrast (for example) to the current situation of stepping off a fast comfortable inter-city train and getting into a slow, cramped and bumpy Pacer. In addition to improving speeds on the main lines, the strategy seeks to tackle the equally important task of significantly improving performance on the secondary lines.

The main elements affecting journey times are top speed, acceleration, braking and the time spent at stations. All of these depend on the design of trains: top speed and braking are also heavily influenced by the characteristics of the network. These network aspects are considered here.

Top speed is fundamentally limited by the curvature of the route. Centrifugal force presses outwards on trains and passengers as they round a curve, the force increasing as the speed increases. For the speeds and curves involved, this is not a safety consideration but a matter of passenger comfort. Tilting trains, such as British Rail's APT of the 1980s and the *Pendolino* recently introduced on the West Coast main line, reduce the lateral forces experienced by passengers when negotiating curves; they can thus go faster on curved routes.

For reasons to be explained, the proposed strategy has a non-tilting train. This means that it can only travel really fast on relatively straight routes, but there are significant distances of those on the network. Other route characteristics as well as curves can also limit speeds. Bridges, viaducts and unstable ground may reduce the rigidity of the track foundations and result in speed restrictions. Limited clearance to lineside structures and aerodynamic effects in narrow tunnels may also necessitate local reductions in speed. In addition, there is little point in authorising high speed on a section of line that is close to a station at which all services stop. The achievable speeds will depend on the acceleration and braking characteristics of the trains, and distances from speed-restricted sections.

As will be described later, the proposed electric trains are designed for a top speed of 150mph, whereas diesel trains remain restricted to 125mph. Consequently, only the electrified routes contain sections authorised for speeds faster than 125mph, as shown in green in *Figure 6*. They are based on typical expected train performance characteristics and estimates of route curvature from looking at maps. In most cases, the constraints caused by existing speed restrictions are retained, but in a few places infrastructure improvements to eliminate those limitations are assumed. A notable example is the Welwyn viaduct and tunnels on the East Coast main line, where the route narrows to two tracks carrying the heavy traffic levels of both the main line and Cambridge routes. Widening of the section has been discussed for half a century but nothing has been done, and somehow the operators manage to live with this bottleneck. A new viaduct and tunnels for the main line are assumed, with a design speed of 150mph.

On the West Coast main line routes out of Euston, tilting *Pendolino* trains are assumed to be predominant; consequently more sections are authorised for high speed running there than the route curvature would permit for the non-tilting train described in this strategy. For the remainder of the network, the sections marked in green in *Figure 6* are suitable for top speeds in the 130 to 150mph range, using the electric inter-city train to be described. Since a typical train would be able to accelerate up to 130mph in around seven miles from a standing start, even medium-distance high speed sections would still help towards reducing journey times.

Another constraint on top speed is braking. A major factor in the then revolutionary introduction of the HST in the 1970s was its improved braking characteristics, allowing it to stop from 125mph in the same distance as a conventional train from 100mph. This allowed the HST to go faster without altering the signalling. Clearly, the new train needs to have the same braking capability as an HST to achieve operation at speeds up to 125mph without modifying the signalling.

What should be done for the 150mph sections though? This speed could be achieved by yet more effective braking on a new train. However, a higher rate of deceleration would impose higher forces on the track, which is undesirable from the points of view of track wear, maintenance costs and safety. In any case, the deceleration rate is limited by the available adhesion between the train and track under poor rail conditions, and stopping distances are calculated assuming a value of only 9%g (g is the acceleration due to gravity). Especially at higher speeds, where the kinetic energy of the train is substantially greater, this deceleration figure should be kept to a low value to reduce longitudinal track forces. Clearly, this means that stopping distances

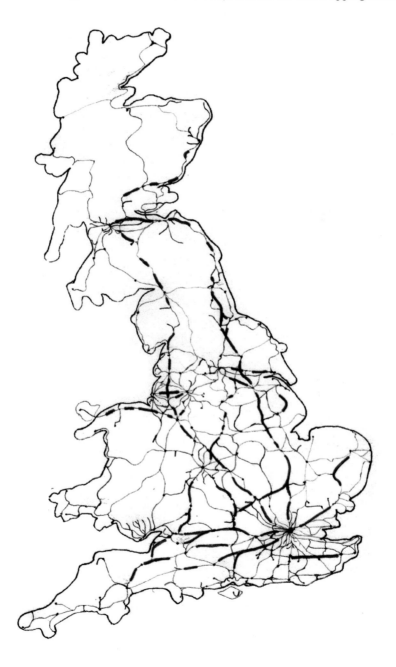

Figure 6: *High speed lines 2035. Sections authorized for 130–150 mph in green.*

need to be significantly extended where speeds greater than 125mph are contemplated. The signalling for such areas needs to be altered to allow this extra stopping distance as economically as possible.

The proposed strategy doubles the stopping distance for 150mph areas. This makes it easy to alter the signalling to convert a 125mph section to 150mph; alternate signals are removed and the remaining ones interlocked in conventional fashion. Consequently, each section is twice as long as before and this allows the train twice the distance in which to stop. In addition, the TPWS (Train Protection and Warning System) balises (transponders) need to be spaced slightly further apart to allow for the higher speed. Erect a new '150' speed restriction sign and the signalling job is complete.

At present, operating agreements make cab-signalling mandatory at speeds over 125mph. The main reason for the rule is that higher speeds with conventional signal spacing give greater demands on drivers; they need to observe signals and cancel AWS (Automatic Warning Signal) indications more frequently. With conventional signal spacing at 150mph, AWS prompts requiring the driver's reaction would come along in only 67% of the time than is the case at the traditional 100mph, and that is rightly considered to be too onerous.

With the proposed approach, however, drivers have a less frenetic life, with only half of the AWS indications to cancel in the distance travelled. Put another way, at 150mph, AWS bells and beeps come along about 1.7 times more slowly than they used to do on the same route at 125mph. Other issues remain, for example the sighting times of signals in foggy conditions are reduced by 17%, but these issues are already covered by the existing AWS and TPWS systems.

The strategy does result in a reduction of line capacity, of course, but this is not as bad as might first appear. The number of sections is halved, but since trains are going faster they clear sections quicker. For example, a route originally designed for a five-minute headway at 100mph converts to a seven-minute headway route at 150mph. Signalling costs should be significantly reduced, as the number of signals is halved, with entirely conventional indications.

On the more heavily-trafficked 150mph corridors shown in *Figure 6*, four tracks are often available to keep slower freight and other trains clear of the 150mph lines. Most two track 150mph sections have lesser demands on track capacity, or alternative routes are available for slower trains. Consequently, there are few locations on the network where this economical approach would be a real problem.

It may be that cab signalling will be introduced network-wide in due course anyway with the European Rail Traffic Management System (ERTMS) project. However, there seems to be no good reason why 150mph operation could not be introduced using conventional signals, AWS and TPWS methods in the meantime by following the proposed strategy.

The 150mph sections are present when the route is electrified (or will be by 2035) and where the route curvature and other speed limits make it practical to go at that speed. No account is taken of the commercial incentive to go faster on a given route, but most 150mph sections are on main lines with high traffic levels. It is expected that the additional revenue generated from reducing journey times with higher speeds would well justify, in time, the modest cost of the signalling alterations proposed. With the train design philosophy to be described, there should be no need to upgrade track for 150mph beyond the standards required for a high quality ride at 125mph with present trains. Consequently, 150mph operation should not be dramatically more expensive for the infrastructure providers in future than 125mph operation is now.

Chapter 3

Reasons for a new train design

At this point it is worth recalling the objectives of the strategy, before considering alternative train designs to satisfy them. In addition to the faster speeds already mentioned, the intention is to improve comfort and to ease access for the passenger, making train travel a more enjoyable experience. From the train operators' point of view, the train needs to have flexibility to match service provision to demand, and must have acceptable running and maintenance costs in relation to the level of performance available. For an inter-city type of train, the main specification points are as follows:

1. Maximum speed of 150mph.
2. High passenger comfort (low noise and vibration, good view etc.).
3. Good space per seat (width and spacing).
4. Ease of access (good door positions and floors level with platforms).
5. Flexibility to alter capacity to demand.
6. Energy efficiency consistent with sufficient performance.
7. Low running costs consistent with sufficient performance.
8. Easy adaptation between electric and diesel operation.

Is it necessary to have a new train design to meet these requirements? The simple answer is yes, of course, otherwise this book would not have been written. To understand why, consider various candidate trains, existing and proposed, to see whether they satisfy these eight specification points.

First, the **Pendolino** tilting electric train, recently introduced on the West Coast main line:

1. Possibly. Although designed for 140mph, it could probably be pushed to 150mph from a braking point of view. However, the relatively stiff bogie suspensions might cause concern due to potential track damage at that speed.
2. No. Noise and vibration due to distributed power concept with powered bogies under the coaches.
3. No. Narrow body at higher levels due to tilt facility.
4. No. Conventional door positions and retractable steps.
5. No. Fixed formation train.
6. Yes.
7. No. High-tech train with tilt facility and multiple motors and drives to maintain.
8. No. Not designed for change of motive power.

Plate 5: *The Pendolino tilting trains were introduced to the West Coast main line in 2007, allowing the curves on this route to be taken at a higher speed. Although these trains are designed for 140 mph, the expensively-rebuilt route still has currently a 125 mph speed restriction. This Pendolino has just arrived at Glasgow Central after running the 401 miles from London Euston in 5 hours, an average speed of 80 mph.*

Second, the ***Class 91 and Mk. 4 Coaches*** non-tilting locomotive-hauled electric train used on the East Coast main line since 1991 (once known as *InterCity 225* due to the originally planned top speed of 225 km/h):

1.   No. Designed for 140mph, but axle load of 21 tonnes now considered too high for such speeds in Britain (although accepted elsewhere).
2.   Yes.
3.   Partly. The coaches were designed for tilt and are fairly narrow at the higher levels.
4.   No. Conventional door spacing and floor level.
5.   Yes, in theory. Formation could be changed, but remains fixed in practice.
6.   Partly. No regenerative braking to improve efficiency, although potential savings are not very significant for a high speed long-distance service.
7.   Yes, since reliability improvements, not especially high-tech.
8.   Yes, in theory. No locomotive changes to diesel in practice at present.

Plate 6: *Since the electrification of the East Coast main line in 1991 the principal inter city trains have comprised the 6000 hp Class 91 locomotives and Mark 4 coaches. These were originally marketed as the InterCity 225 train, a reference to their 140 mph design speed in kilometres per hour. In fact, they remain restricted to 125 mph. This one has arrived at London King's Cross on a service from Edinburgh Waverley, a journey of 393 miles taking 4¾ hours with 10 stops, an average of 82 mph.*

Third, the diesel **HST (InterCity 125)**, British Rail's masterpiece from the 1970s:

1. No.
2. Yes.
3. Yes, originally. Refurbishment has reduced seat spacing giving lower comfort levels more recently.
4. No. Conventional door spacing and high floor.
5. No. A fixed formation train.
6. Partly. New diesel engines have improved efficiency and reduced pollution.
7. No. Two diesel engines to maintain.
8. No.

Plate 7: *The HSTs have diesel power cars at each end of the train, allowing the coaches to be free of their noise and vibration and to provide a smooth ride. More modern long distance trains on the British network have not (so far) matched HST standards of comfort. This HST is arriving at Perth on a service from Inverness to London King's Cross, a total journey of over 580 miles. It accomplishes this in under 8 hours, at an average speed of 73 mph.*

Fourth, the *Voyager / Meridian* type of train used on the Cross Country and Midland routes:

1. No.
2. No. Diesel engines under the coach floor produce much noise and vibration.
3. No. Coach bodies designed for tilt, whether tilting or not, so rather narrow.
4. No. Conventional door spacing and floor level.
5. No. A fixed formation train.
6. Partly. Multiple diesel engines provide redundancy for improved reliability, but may not be as efficient as one big diesel engine.
7. No. Many diesel engines and transmissions to maintain, on every coach.
8. No, at present. Could be converted to electric or hybrid traction more easily than other fixed formation trains though.

Plate 8: *The Voyager diesel electric multiple units are capable of 125 mph with high acceleration, as they have a 750 hp diesel engine under every coach. This imparts considerable noise and vibration to the passenger accommodation, making them less comfortable for long inter-city journeys than the HSTs and older locomotive hauled trains they replaced. This one pauses at York on a service from Birmingham to Newcastle, a journey of 186 miles which takes 3½ hours with 10 intermediate stops, an average of 54 mph.*

Fifth, the *Eurostar* train used on international services (and briefly on the East Coast route):

1. Yes.
2. Yes.
3. Yes.
4. Partly. Even door spacing, but floor not level with platform.
5. No. A fixed formation train.
6. Partly. Appropriate for 186mph, but overpowered and not efficient for 150mph.
7. No. A complex multi-voltage, multi-system train.
8. No.

Plate 9: *The 186 mph Eurostar trains were introduced in 1994 with the opening of the Channel Tunnel. This one catches the late afternoon sunshine as it whizzes across the Medway Viaduct near Rochester on a service from Paris Gare du Nord to London St Pancras International, a 306 mile journey accomplished in 2 hours 21 minutes at an average speed of 130 mph. Very high speeds do need more energy to overcome air resistance: this train has 16,400 hp to accelerate its 752 tonnes.*

19

Sixth, the *Javelin* high speed commuter train for services from St Pancras to Kent starting soon:

1. Possibly. Stiff suspensions might be a concern on the established network at 150mph.
2. No. A distributed power train with powered bogies under the coaches.
3. Partly. Designed as a commuter train, but seat pitch could be increased for greater comfort in an inter-city application.
4. Partly. Even door spacing, but floor not level with platform.
5. No. A fixed formation train.
6. Yes.
7. Yes.
8. No.

Plate 10: *One of the justifications for the Channel Tunnel Rail Link, now known as High Speed 1, was the possibility to introduce a fast commuter link to London from Kent. The creation of this new infrastructure was also a factor in London's successful bid to host the 2012 Olympic Games, with the commuter trains offering a fast 'Javelin' link to the games site at Stratford. In advance of the full service, this Javelin 140 mph electric multiple unit waits at London St Pancras International on a 'preview' service to Dover. The same distributed power technology is used in the proposed Super Express Train (SET).*

As can be seen, none of these existing trains come close to meeting all the requirements. A new train design is needed. Do the two main proposals being advocated at present satisfy all the specification points requested in this strategy?

Firstly there is the **SET (Super Express Train)** proposed by the DfT:

1. Possibly. Currently 140mph is talked about, but stiff suspensions might be a concern at 150mph.
2. No. A distributed power train with powered bogies under the coaches.
3. No. Relatively narrow body due to 26m length.
4. No. Conventional door spacing and floor level.
5. No. A fixed formation train.
6. Yes. Regenerative braking and battery storage to re-use energy for traction.
7. No. A high-tech train with many drives and complications like traction power bus lines.
8. Yes. Diesel, electric and hybrid options, although the hybrid version looks underpowered in diesel mode.

Second, there is the **Conventional Bo-Bo electric locomotive-hauled train** adapted from standard modern European designs to fit the smaller British loading gauge:

1. No. Locomotive axle load too high for 150mph in UK. 125mph possible.
2. Yes.
3. Yes.
4. No. Conventional door spacing and floor level.
5. Yes.
6. Yes for electric operation. No for diesel haulage (no regenerative braking into battery storage).
7. Yes.
8. Yes.

Neither proposal meets the requirements either. The conventional Bo-Bo electric locomotive-hauled train gets fairly close, but the limited maximum speed of 125mph is a particular disappointment.

This leads to the obvious conclusion that none of the existing trains, or the proposals the author knows about, will satisfy all the desired objectives. Something better is needed: hence the proposed concept described in the next chapter.

Chapter 4

Concept choice for the new train

The concept of the new train emerges quite naturally from consideration of the objectives mentioned in the last chapter. No new technologies are involved, but the 'architecture' of the train is considered in a slightly non-conventional way. Mostly, however, the choices are straightforward pragmatic engineering decisions regarding the best course of action to meet requirements. As a major need is for a design suitable for replacing the HST, the long-distance inter-city type of train is considered first.

One fundamental choice is whether the train should be 'locomotive-hauled' or 'distributed power'. The essence of this is whether the passenger-carrying vehicles provide traction or not. In a conventional train, the locomotive provides traction, and the coaches are unpowered 'trailers'. Although it may not appear to be so, the HST is also 'locomotive-hauled' in this sense; the two diesel power cars at either end of the train provide traction, and the coaches are unpowered.

In contrast, the 'distributed power' train concept uses the passenger coaches to provide traction. Some of the coaches may be powered, or all of them. Diesel and electric multiple units come into this category.

From the passenger's perspective, a locomotive-hauled train is superior to a distributed power one. Since there are no traction motors, drives or diesel engines on the coaches in a locomotive-hauled concept, all these sources of noise and vibration are eliminated near the passenger environment. The smoothness of ride is also better, as the coach suspension does not have to deal with traction forces and can be 'softer' in consequence. This effect can be observed, for example, on a *Class 455* electric multiple unit by comparing the rough standard of ride in the one powered coach with the silky smoothness of the three trailer coaches.

Of course it is possible to have a badly designed locomotive-hauled train with a noisier passenger environment and rougher ride than a well designed distributed power train. That is quite difficult though! However hard the designers try, the best coach for a distributed power concept cannot match the noise and vibration performance of a locomotive-hauled coach, which does not have to cope with those problems. The locomotive-hauled concept also has fewer coach design constraints, as there is no need to find space for the traction components.

The locomotive-hauled concept also means that the coaches are simpler and cheaper than equivalent distributed power ones. From the perspective of the coach design, the only involvement in traction is providing adequate strength to transmit traction forces in either direction through the couplings, and carrying control signals between the locomotive and driving trailer or power cars at either end of the train.

If the train has a reasonably large capacity, maintenance costs should be lower for a locomotive-hauled concept. Rather than many small drives, motors or engines, there are a few bigger ones. Also, these are concentrated into one or two relatively high-tech vehicles, simplifying maintenance regimes rather than having to do complex tasks on the whole train.

Adapting train capacity to demand is easier with a locomotive-hauled train. Coaches can be added or removed as necessary during the day or for different routes, and as they are simpler there are few interfacing problems. Different kinds of vehicles (such as restaurant or sleeping cars) can be added to trains as appropriate. This contrasts with the distributed power concept, where a train may only be able to operate at all with a particular combination of vehicles. Consequently, it is often a fixed formation train, with gross over-capacity at times of low demand.

Conversely, if the distributed power train is designed to be a modular multiple unit, so that it can readily adapt its capacity, several driving cabs are needed with all their controls. These occupy space and cost money. For high speeds the multiple unit concept also results in the uncomfortable choice between nice streamlined front ends without intercommunication between units being possible (resulting in duplicated refreshment facilities and increased staffing), or making drivers sit in cramped cabs adjacent to corridor connections having poor aerodynamic characteristics.

Changing traction type between electric and diesel is easier with a locomotive-hauled approach; it is only necessary to swap the locomotive in conventional fashion. This can avoid inefficiencies such as unused diesel engines (whether underfloor engines or separate generator cars) being transported around the electrified network.

In the case of major breakdown, the locomotive-hauled train is often easier to deal with too; most probably the fault will be on the complex locomotive rather than a simple coach, so rescue can be performed by changing the locomotive rather than having to get passengers off a completely disabled train.

A further advantage of the locomotive-hauled concept is that the performance specification of the train is less dependent on the coaches but more influenced by the locomotive. The same coach design can speed along a fast main line behind an electric locomotive in a long train, or meander more slowly down a curving branch line in a short train behind a low powered diesel locomotive. The coach provides an appropriate level of technology and cost for both applications. It also facilitates through services to less popular locations if desired.

The distributed power concept does have some advantages. There is no need for a separate locomotive, and for a lower capacity short train that might be a significant capital cost reduction. Also, potentially acceleration can be greater as the powered vehicles have a higher proportion of the train's total weight, improving adhesion. These advantages particularly come into play for a short-distance commuter train, which needs high acceleration for a reasonable average speed when there are closely spaced stops.

For a high speed long-distance train, however, these advantages of distributed power diminish. Normally the train will have a high passenger capacity, so the need for an additional vehicle (the locomotive) is less important from a cost point of view. For a given performance the same installed power is needed somewhere, so there is not so much difference between the costs of the two concepts. Since trains have a long life (as they should have for environmental reasons, given the materials and energy required to manufacture them), the original capital cost of purchase becomes less significant, and maintenance and running costs become more critical. The whole life cost of a locomotive-hauled solution may become less than a distributed power one as there are fewer motors and drives to maintain.

Regarding acceleration, the higher adhesion of the distributed power train is only valuable at lower speeds; as the speed increases, power becomes the limiting factor, not adhesion. As long as adhesion is sufficient (which it is, as will be shown later) the locomotive-hauled solution will perform just as well for a high speed train.

Another factor to consider is the effect on track wear. The distributed power concept permits rapid acceleration and braking, but the consequently high forces require relatively stiff suspensions throughout the train. Apparently some evidence suggests that the locomotive-hauled concept with higher axle loads on the locomotive but lower loads and more compliant suspensions on the coaches could cause less track wear overall than an equivalent distributed power train. The jury seems to be out on this question at the moment, but clearly the latest research, practical experience and implications need to be made better known than they are at present. The precise conditions of measurement are critical to form any solid conclusions about a future optimum solution for low track costs.

Given all the above factors, the decision is easy: the concept must be a locomotive-hauled train and not a distributed power one.

The next question is whether to have tilting or not. A tilting train can reduce journey times substantially on a curving route: for a straight route it makes no difference. A significant disadvantage of tilting is that the coach body profile has to be narrower approaching the ceiling to give clearance on a curve: this gives a cramped feeling compared with a non-tilting coach.

In addition, the tilt mechanism adds complication, which increases both capital and maintenance costs. There are costs involved in the network too, with the installation of systems that authorise the tilt under appropriate conditions.

A further disadvantage of tilting is the reduced stability perceived by passengers, especially when standing or walking through the train. Although modern tilting train technology has greatly improved the situation compared with British Rail's early experiments in the 1980s, the dynamic characteristics of the tilt mechanism do increase the 'liveliness' of the ride when entering and leaving curved sections of route. These dynamic influences are also perceptible through the difference between a passenger's sense of balance and the observed passing scenery. One way of reducing the effect is to have small windows, which, with the narrower body profile, produce an even more unappealing aircraft-like passenger environment.

The most commercially significant curving route in Britain is the West Coast main line, which has recently been re-equipped with the *Pendolino* tilting train. These will probably remain in service for the next thirty years at least, so there is no need for a new train there. The Midland main line might benefit from a tilting train, but most journeys are relatively short so dramatic reductions in journey time would not be achieved. The core part of the Great Western main line is very straight, so tilting there would be no help. Substantial stretches of the Cross Country inter-city routes are straight enough for tilt to contribute little.

Some other routes are rather curved, such as Manchester to Leeds, and Perth to Inverness. However, most services on these sections are through trains from places on straighter alignments, so the overall benefit of tilting is quite small.

Consequently, for maximum spaciousness and avoidance of cost the proposed strategy is a non-tilting train.

Having decided that the concept is a non-tilting locomotive-hauled train, the next step is to determine the general form of the design and some of its major parameters.

Since it is not desirable to waste time running locomotives round the train at termini to be at the front again after reversal, and in many locations run-round facilities no longer exist anyway, the proposed concept is a push-pull train. There is a locomotive at one end, then a variable number of coaches, and finally a driving trailer at the other end.

The maximum length and capacity of the train need to be decided. In the past, long trains of sixteen coaches or so have been used, and the practice is still common for medium- and long-distance services in some other countries. For higher speeds there is also an advantage in making trains long, as the power consumed starts to be dominated by overcoming air resistance and much of this is expended in shifting air at the front end. Consequently, long high speed trains need less energy per seat than short trains. However, in this case only medium speeds of 150mph are involved, not the 186mph of a Eurostar, so the energy efficiency incentive to make trains very long is less pronounced.

There are also practical limits to the length of trains in many locations, as track layouts have been simplified and concourses at termini extended. Finally, commercial considerations often preclude long trains. On a route with moderate traffic density, an infrequent service of long trains can be expected to attract much less custom than a more frequent service. To make efficient use of resources, the trains will be shorter to match capacity to demand.

All things considered, a maximum train capacity of around 600 passengers seems to be a reasonable compromise. Using low-density high-comfort seating arrangements, accommodating first and standard class passengers, and providing facilities for refreshments, toilets, wheelchairs, prams, luggage, bicycles and staff results in a train about 340m long. As a comparison, this would be approximately equivalent in length to a train with thirteen *Mark 4* coaches plus the locomotive and driving trailer.

Traditionally, individual coaches with a capacity of forty to seventy passengers can be added to a train formation, but such a close matching of capacity to demand is considered unnecessary. For a quality long-distance service, all passengers should get seats: since day-to-day fluctuations in loading are difficult to predict, a moderate over-provision of seating capacity will be normal. Instead, the main part of the maximum length train is divided into six sections, roughly equivalent to being able to add or remove pairs of conventional coaches. Each section may have one or more accommodation types according to requirements. The seating capacity increment is between seventy-two and 120, depending on the mix of classes.

A consequence of the strategy, with a standard locomotive design, is that the power to weight ratio (and thus acceleration capability) of the train increases as the length reduces. Often this is exactly what is needed.

On a busy route, the service will usually be divided into limited stop trains running at sustained high speeds for long distances to the main traffic centres in big cities, interspersed with stopping trains serving intermediate stations in smaller cities or towns.

The stopping trains will obviously be slower, and consequently less popular with those travelling to the main centres. If they are too slow, there is also the risk that the stopping trains will get in the way of the following limited stop trains.

In the proposed strategy, the stopping trains will be shorter as they need less capacity. This gives them greater acceleration, allowing them to get away faster from their intermediate stops. Consequently, their average speed is higher and less different from the limited stop trains. This in turn eases the timetabling problems of interleaving services.

The concept also makes stopping trains more attractive for travellers to the main centres, allowing them to make a greater contribution to the popularity of the service on the route as a whole. There is no need to have different equipment for stopping trains, and services to intermediate stations can be significantly improved. This in turn can help to reduce road traffic congestion as passengers make more use of their local stations, rather than driving to a traffic-delay-prone main centre with uncertain car parking capacity to get a faster train service (or more likely driving all the way to their destinations).

A further advantage of the approach is the flexibility it gives for train service patterns. Usually, early morning and late evening trains will be lightly loaded, and having the daytime sequence of limited stop and stopping services would be over-provision for the demand at those times. Instead, a service of short stopping trains only can be run then, which with their higher acceleration can still give attractive end-to-end journey times while maintaining services to intermediate stations. As the day progresses, coaches can simply be added or removed as necessary to give a closer matching to demand, and to save energy as well.

In addition to the above advantages, the strategy permits very short trains (down to one-sixth of the maximum capacity, with about 100 seats). This should be particularly useful when a long-distance train splits into several sections to serve remoter parts of the network, hauled perhaps by low-powered diesel locomotives.

Chapter 5

Components of
the inter-city train

Having described the general form of the proposed long-distance train, the individual vehicles it comprises are now considered.

Electric locomotives

The electric locomotives are specified to haul or propel full-length trains on the principal routes at speeds up to 150mph. Since full-length trains will tend to be used mainly on services travelling long distances between stops at sustained high speeds, a high level of acceleration is not especially beneficial in reducing journey times in these circumstances: it is the top speed that matters most. In fact, as mentioned above, it is desirable to limit track forces at the higher speeds anyway, which includes acceleration forces as well as braking forces.

The proposed concept matches the acceleration capability of an HST for a full-length train. A nine-plus-two car East Coast HST weighs 460 tonnes, and is accelerated by a combined 4,500hp (3.4MW). Consequently, the power to weight ratio is nearly 10hp/tonne. The new train weighs about 570 tonnes, so the installed power of the locomotive should be around 6,000hp (4.5MW) for the same acceleration capability as an HST: this is the same as a *Class 91*.

More curving inter-city routes often have shorter journeys (for example, the Midland main line compared with the East Coast). Both of these factors will encourage the use of shorter trains there, to give better acceleration away from speed-restricted sections and to provide more frequent services for closely-spaced main centres. A more typical train for such routes might be two-thirds of the full length, with a seating capacity of about 400. Such a train is 240m long, and the power to weight ratio improves to 14hp/tonne.

Since track wear is strongly influenced by axle loads, the locomotive proposed is a six-axle design of either Co-Co or Bo-Bo-Bo configuration. This gives an axle load of about 15 tonnes, substantially less than the 17.5 tonnes of each HST power car. It is also quite a bit less than the 21 tonnes axle load of a *Class 91* electric locomotive (supposedly designed for 140mph but never permitted to go at that speed in normal service), and a lot less than the 22.5 tonnes of the *Class 67* diesel designed for 125mph.

The locomotive is equipped with a substantial regenerative braking capability, which returns power to the overhead line when decelerating, reducing overall energy consumption. It is true that for a long-distance fast train with few stops and a flat route, most power will be consumed in overcoming air and vehicle resistance, and the percentage of energy that can be recovered in braking is very small. There are other benefits, however; wear on disc brakes throughout the train is reduced and consequently maintenance costs go down. As will be seen, there are other substantial advantages for the rolling stock.

Trains having more frequent stops or traversing steeper gradients will naturally have a higher proportion of the energy consumed in accelerating or climbing hills, but much of this energy can be recovered by regenerative braking when decelerating or descending gradients. The effect is to reduce the energy consumption caused by train weight. Consequently, there is less need to be especially frugal in the weight of passenger coaches, with consequent improvements in smoothness of ride and less noise in the vehicles.

The electrical system of the locomotive which provides regenerative braking is arranged to take full advantage of the power capability of the mechanical components: the wheels, suspension, transmission and motors. Of course, the amount of deceleration of the whole train that can be provided by regenerative braking from the locomotive is limited by adhesion, in the same way as is the amount of acceleration.

The gentler deceleration from 150mph proposed in this strategy will, however, fit within the capabilities imposed by these limits. Under the standard specification for low adhesion conditions, deceleration from 125mph to a stop remains at 9%g; however the average deceleration from 150 to 125mph works out at only 3.9%g with the extra stopping distance of the strategy. In practice, there is no sudden change of braking rate at 125mph: braking starts gently at full speed and increases gradually as the speed reduces. This gives a smooth stopping pattern as well as improving the efficiency of recovering the energy by restraining peak regeneration currents to manageable levels. At lower speeds, when the braking rate is highest, disc brakes throughout the train provide most of the braking effort, but by that time much of the kinetic energy of the train has been recovered. This eases the burden on the train disc brakes significantly, compared to a conventional approach without regenerative braking. In fact, as will be described, further braking assistance comes from another source.

Naturally the locomotive is equipped with a rheostatic braking option as well, to dissipate the energy in the event of pantograph or overhead line failure or network receptivity problems.

The drive and suspension system of the locomotive will be better than a *Class 91*, to reduce track wear and consequently to lower track maintenance costs. This is easy to say and less easy to do: track damage is a complex function involving axle loads, unsprung weights, component dynamics, transient acceleration forces, plastic deformation of metal, fatigue crack propagation, track hardness profiles, wheel profiles and wear, track curvature and uneven wear, lateral oscillation modes, track position accuracy, trackbed resilience and goodness knows what else. Nevertheless, the situation is eased considerably compared with the *Class 91* concept by having lower axle loads and by specifying lower acceleration and deceleration forces at high speeds. In addition, suitable control systems can adjust the tractive effort, braking effort and suspension dynamics characteristics as functions of speed and track conditions to produce optimum results, improving the available adhesion under less than ideal conditions.

The above factors should make electric locomotive haulage at 150mph a practical proposition, although careful analysis by track and vehicle dynamics experts will be needed to convince many that it can be done at a reasonable cost. A complete analysis of the situation, including the latest research and evidence from high speed locomotive haulage elsewhere, should be in the public domain so that people throughout the railway industry can satisfy themselves that the optimum strategic decisions are being taken regarding train speeds.

A locomotive with these improved facilities will have a significantly higher capital cost than a straightforward 125mph Bo-Bo design, and this might seem a serious disadvantage. However the whole system, not just the locomotive, needs to be considered before it is possible to decide the most economical solution overall. The more expensive locomotive will cause less track wear at all speeds, giving lower running costs for the network, which should be reflected in lower access charges. It will consume less energy and cause less wear in disc brakes, reducing train running and maintenance costs. Because of the higher top speed, it will generate more revenue and require fewer trains to provide the same service frequency. Some rather complex calculations need to be done, with estimates of traffic levels and economic conditions, before the optimum strategic decisions can be taken for specifying the locomotive.

The locomotive proposed is single-ended like an HST power car; in other words it has a cab at one end with a streamlined outline, the other end being 'blunt' for coupling to the coaches without a gap to cause aerodynamic drag. Although the locomotive will always be coupled to the train the right way round in traffic, it is necessary to have full flexibility to run in both directions for shunting and light engine movements. The concept is not a fixed formation train; the locomotive might be serviced in a different location from the coaches in some cases, and almost certainly will have a different maintenance cycle. In order to achieve this bi-directional capability, a video camera is activated to provide a forward view on a screen in the single driver's cab when running as a light engine with the blunt end first.

As well as reducing cost by avoiding the need for a second driving cab and all its duplicated controls, the video camera concept has further advantages. Additional video cameras in strategic locations (adjacent to the couplings and at the sides of the locomotive) allow the driver to perform shunting movements more safely without leaning out of cab windows, changing ends, or relying on signals from other staff.

Such facilities should also help to make alterations of vehicle formation more rapid, when a train is split in sections to serve lower density routes and/or there is a change between electric and diesel traction.

Since only those long-distance routes having high traffic density will be electrified in the medium term, one standard electric locomotive design to the above specification is considered sufficient, at least for the first few years of implementing the strategy. A lower powered version of the above locomotive can be considered for hauling shorter trains as electrification is extended to less busy long-distance routes in the longer term. This would need to be substantially cheaper in both capital and running costs to offset the flexibility and performance available using one standard locomotive suitable for any train. If it is worthwhile to make such a second electric locomotive design, the specifications of regenerative braking and 150mph maximum speed would be retained.

Diesel locomotives

Diesel locomotives will be used on lower density parts of the inter-city network where there are generally fewer topographical opportunities for 150mph running and less commercial incentive to go at that speed. In the absence of an overhead line, there are also fewer benefits from implementing regenerative braking, due to the cost of energy storage. Consequently, locomotive braking probably will be rheostatic at best. In the light of these factors it is considered sufficient to limit top speeds to 125mph when using diesel haulage.

For medium length trains, a 3,200hp (2.4MW) 125mph design would be appropriate, similar to a *Class 67*. This does have a rather high axle load of 22.5 tonnes, though, so a design having higher power with a Co-Co configuration would be preferable technically. It is doubtful whether there is sufficient need for such a locomotive to justify a new design, however, and its life may be limited as electrification gradually renders it superfluous.

Most trains requiring diesel haulage will be much shorter, and in that context a locomotive of about 2,200hp (1.6MW) power and 125mph would be ideal. This is the same specification as an HST power car. Since these have been recently re-engined although they are old, they can certainly be used in the medium term to power shorter trains. Over 100 HST power cars would become available if the Midland and Great Western routes were electrified, so no new diesel locomotives of this power would be needed in the first few years of implementing the proposed strategy.

Pairs of HST power cars could be used to provide higher power where necessary for the few cases of long trains on non-electrified routes. This retains the flexibility to split them for powering more short trains.

In the longer term, a more modern diesel locomotive using the same concept as the HST power car is proposed, unless electrification advances sufficiently to make it unnecessary. Such a diesel locomotive could have higher power for improved acceleration, but it is probably not worth designing it for faster speeds than 125mph.

Driving trailers

The driving trailer at the opposite end of the train from the locomotive is of one standard type, regardless of the type of traction or length of train. Like the locomotive, it has a driving cab at the streamlined end. It has a conventional four axle Bo-Bo wheel configuration.

The driving trailer is robustly constructed to meet safety standards of crashworthiness, and also it is fairly heavy to remain on the track in the event of such accidents as collisions with road vehicles on level crossings. It has an axle load of 15 tonnes. There is no passenger seating in the driving trailer, but it includes service facilities needed by the train as a whole.

A large van space is provided to accommodate bicycles. Limited stop trains between big cities can be expected to attract a smaller proportion of cyclist passengers than a stopping train used for shorter hops between intermediate stations. Consequently, the provision of a fixed number of cycle spaces per train, regardless of the length of the train, matches the expected demand quite naturally. Putting the cycle space right at the end of the train (always the same end on a given route) keeps the movements of cycles on and off the train well out of the way of alighting and boarding passengers, easing the mêlée on busy platforms. Sufficient cycle space should be freely available without reservation to reduce some of the problems in using this environmentally-friendly mode of travel.

Further van space is provided for especially bulky luggage (which will probably not be much used as there is sufficient space for most items in the coaches), catering supplies, refreshment trolleys, rubbish sacks, etc.

The driving trailer also contains a guards' compartment. In addition to accommodation and seating for the train staff, and equipment such as ticket machines, this compartment has train monitoring equipment and communication facilities. It is provided with an enquiry window for passenger queries.

At the end of the driving trailer, nearest to the corridor connection from the adjacent coach, is a passenger service facility. This area contains drinks and snacks vending machines, complementary to other refreshment facilities provided on the train (or as a substitute for them on lightly loaded services where even refreshment trolleys are not provided). This is also the area for racks of promotional brochures, timetables, free magazines and papers, tourist information leaflets etc., which passengers can take back to their seats in the train. The presence of the adjacent guards' compartment, with a suitable window to observe activity, should deter the misuse of the unstaffed passenger service facilities.

The driving trailer provides regenerative braking for the train to assist the locomotive. Since its motors are not normally used for traction, and braking periods are not continuous (for stopping they are usually over in two minutes at most), they can be smaller and cheaper than the traction motors of the locomotive. The brake forces that can be applied per wheel are the same as the electric locomotive, since the axle loads are the same. Consequently, with eight wheels out of the twenty involved in regenerative braking, the driving trailer recovers 40% of the regenerative braking energy of an electrically powered train.

To avoid the cost and complications of high voltage or traction power bus lines through the train, the energy recovered by regenerative braking in the driving trailer is not returned to the overhead line. Of course, in diesel operated areas there is no overhead line anyway. Instead, the recovered energy is used to charge local batteries. These batteries have sufficient capacity to absorb the energy generated by a stop from 150mph in a full-length (maximum weight) train.

When the batteries are charged to a sufficient level, they are then used to power the 'hotel bus' of the train (which drives the lights and air-conditioning) instead of the usual supply from the locomotive. After they are discharged to a lower level, the locomotive takes over the task of powering the hotel bus again.

Should there be a power failure from the locomotive, the driving trailer can keep the train's lighting and air-conditioning going for a period using this facility. Similarly, when electric locomotives are exchanged for diesel ones or vice versa, the driving trailer maintains power when there is no locomotive coupled to the train.

Of course, a longer train requires more 'hotel power' than a shorter one; but it is also heavier, so more energy is recovered by regenerative braking and the batteries are charged to a greater extent at each stop. This helps towards meeting the greater power demands of the longer train in the event of a fault or when the locomotive is uncoupled.

This strategy also works when a train is split into sections: the locomotive powers one section and the driving trailer the other, from the time of the split until a new driving trailer and new locomotive are attached to the separate parts to continue their journeys.

Another use for the stored energy is to power the driving trailer itself as a locomotive. Only a limited power is available for a limited period, and this facility will be used infrequently during the day, perhaps not at all. Nevertheless, the energy available is ample to allow the driving trailer to shunt coaches into sidings or retrieve them at low speed, which may be more convenient than using the locomotive at the other end of the train when changes of train formation are necessary. The driving trailer is equipped with the same video camera and screen system as the locomotive to permit bidirectional running from the single cab. It also has all the necessary control equipment such as an air compressor to allow it to act independently as a locomotive.

It is also possible to use the driving trailer as additional power to assist the main locomotive for short periods in traffic. This will be particularly useful to provide a boost to acceleration when a train is running late, or to maintain speed where adhesion is especially bad (e.g. due to local leaf fall) and is no longer within the range of the slip and slide control system of the locomotive. Such use will drain the batteries rapidly though, so schedules should be designed assuming traction from the locomotive only. It is purely a short-term get-out-of-trouble facility.

In the event of a train breaking down due to locomotive or overhead line failure, the driving trailer could be used to move the whole train at low speed to the next station in most situations. The possibilities depend on circumstances, especially the level of charge in the batteries, the distance to the next station, and the prevailing gradients. Knowing these factors, the driver has to make a decision as to the best course of action. If the overhead line fails at the bottom of a long uphill gradient on a hot day when the train is running late and the driving trailer has been used as a power booster, the best course of action may be to sit tight and summon assistance, using the remaining battery power to maintain the air-conditioning. Hopefully that unfortunate combination of mishaps will be rare!

Coaches

Those becoming alarmed by the potential cost of the train, with its high-tech locomotive and driving trailer, can start to relax a bit from now on. The strategy deliberately places all the expensive technologies in the locomotive and driving trailer in order to make the coaches relatively simple, low-tech and cost-effective. Since there are many coaches in a train but only one locomotive and one driving trailer, this allows the overall capital cost of the train to come down again to reasonable levels.

Since the coaches are straightforward unpowered 'trailers', extending train formations to accommodate increased traffic levels is cheaper and simpler than it would be for a distributed power strategy. There is full flexibility to add or remove vehicles with accommodation of various kinds according to particular requirements in any combination up to the maximum train length. The technical interfaces of all coaches are the same. This contrasts strongly with a distributed power concept, where particular combinations of vehicles are necessary to provide the appropriate technical resources for a complete train.

According to convenience, trains can be serviced as complete units or separated into sections, for example to fit into depots unable to deal with full-length trains. If coaches have serious faults or are involved in accidents, they can be easily removed and replaced out on the network: this is not a depot task as it would be for a fixed formation train.

The absence of traction motors, gears, drives, air compressors, donkey engines and power conversion units on the coaches eliminates all these sources of noise and vibration. There is no need to find space for such items either. Consequently, design constraints are considerably reduced and it is much easier to provide a quiet, restful and spacious passenger environment. The absence of these items helps to keep vehicle weights (and axle loads) down too.

In this strategy, coach suspensions never need to transmit acceleration forces, and its moderate braking requirements permit conventional disc brakes on the wheels only. Regenerative braking on the locomotive and driving trailer takes care of most high speed braking forces, the disc brakes on the coaches being blended in gradually to provide greater braking effort as speed reduces. Consequently, the coach suspensions can be more compliant than they would be for a powered multiple unit concept, giving a smoother ride as well as causing less track wear.

The coaches are coupled together in articulated groups of three, with a short distance between bogie centres allowing the coach to be wider while maintaining full route availability. This permits the rolling stock to traverse any route for diversions or excursions, or if it is desired to restore through services to some less populated locations through the once common practice of splitting trains.

As well as increasing the width of the coach, the proposed design increases the floor-to-ceiling height of the interior. This gives increased headroom for tall people, and permits level access from platforms.

The 50m long articulated group of three coaches (or 'triplet') is supported on four bogies, and its length is similar to two conventional *Mk. 3* coaches, which also have four bogies. Average axle loads are thus comparable (9 tonnes) as the weight per unit length is similar.

Each coach has five seating modules in standard class, or four in first class. Thus a standard class triplet has three x five x eight = 120 seats using eight seats per module. Other variations include first class only triplets, or composite triplets having some standard and some first class accommodation. Although the coach body structures are identical regardless of the accommodation, different window panels are fitted (with five or four windows) according to class so that all seats have a good view.

The ample seating module dimensions accommodate taller passengers comfortably in well-upholstered seats, together with items of luggage between the seat backs. Both face-to-face and airline style seating is provided, with 2.1m seat pitch for face-to-face seats in standard class and 2.6m in first class. There are substantial luggage racks at both ends of the seating area, on both sides of the coach.

Each seating area contains no more than forty passengers, and has access at both ends. This reduces the potential for tangles between people realising they need to get out at a late stage and those struggling with luggage to find their seats.

The entrance vestibules are above the bogies, more evenly spaced than conventional coaches. This also avoids large gaps between coach doors and platform edges on sharp curves.

Toilets are located at either end of the triplet, on the opposite sides of the entrance vestibules from the seating areas. At one end, two standard toilets are fitted, one on each side of the corridor. The other end has one larger toilet accessible by wheelchair users.

The coach width possible at waist level would be determined by a comprehensive route survey, but about 3.0m looks feasible, 10% wider than the *Mk. 3* design. This would permit standard class seats about 5cm (2in) wider together with an aisle 6cm (2½in) wider.

The lower floor gives level access at standard platform height, some 30cm (12in) lower than usual. Overall, the extra width and height internally result in around 20% greater cross-sectional area compared to a *Mk. 3* coach. In combination with more generous seat spacing and bigger windows aligned well with the seats, this will give a much improved feeling of spaciousness. Better, bigger and squashier seats will reinforce the feeling of unpretentious comfort. Low ambient noise levels will create a relaxed environment, and low vibration will facilitate stretching out and dozing.

The improved comfort, additional space and ease of access should result in a better image for the train operators as promoters of good design.

Inter-city train features summary

Having now outlined the main features of all the vehicles in the train, this is a good point at which to summarise the key elements of the strategy for long-distance inter-city type trains.

Full-length electric trains with 600 seats match the acceleration of an HST with a higher top speed of 150mph, giving significantly faster schedules for long non-stop runs on straight main lines. Shorter electric trains can be chosen using the same equipment to give greater acceleration on curving routes or for services with more frequent stops, giving fast schedules and good energy efficiency.

Medium-length trains, having a capacity of 300 seats, can be hauled by conventional diesel locomotives, and shorter diesel trains can use ex-HST power cars made redundant by electrification. These diesel trains have comparable acceleration to an HST and a 125mph maximum speed.

All train formations can be easily altered out on the network, with combined sections of trains easing congestion on the electrified core routes while facilitating through diesel services to less populated locations.

Where the topography permits a 150mph maximum speed, the strategy allows signalling to be altered very economically.

Facilities are provided to maintain air-conditioning and lighting when locomotives are uncoupled or trains break down, using energy recycled from regenerative braking. In all but the most unfavourable situations, the train can move slowly to the next station in the event of a diesel engine or overhead line failure.

High levels of comfort are provided for passengers, significantly exceeding the best 1970s standards in spaciousness and matching them in low noise and vibration.

Easy level access is provided from standard platforms, without big steps or gaps.

This combination of features seems to be significantly better than any existing train design, from the points of view of both passengers and train operators. Actually achieving all these objectives depends on more detailed analysis, however, so the next step is to consider some numbers to check that the concept will actually work. Train dynamics, energy management and the detailed design of the coaches are particularly important aspects: these are considered in the following chapters.

Chapter 6

Train dynamics

Train weights, lengths, capacity and installed power

Naturally, the weights of vehicles can only be determined accurately when more detailed design work has been done. In order to get a feel for the dynamics and feasibility of the concept, some rough estimates have been made which are moderately challenging but hopefully practicable with careful design.

The six axle 6,000hp (4.5MW) electric locomotives are estimated at 90 tonnes, slightly higher than modern European four axle designs of higher power (84 tonnes and 6MW). It is assumed that the 21 tonne axle load of a standard Bo-Bo design would not be permitted to go faster than 125mph on British track, in contrast to the practice in some other parts of Europe. Since the objective is a maximum speed of 150mph, it is assumed that an axle load of 15 tonnes provided by the six axle design will be low enough to achieve that speed. The low acceleration and deceleration at high speed specified in the strategy, together with high performance suspension and control systems, are other elements in meeting the objective.

Of course, there is no objection to higher power if that can be achieved within an axle load permitting 150mph, but for the sake of argument it is assumed that the power will be constrained somewhat to keep the weight down. The lower power also implies that no additional power supply capacity is needed for the current train frequencies on routes already electrified. A length of about 20m seems reasonable.

Not much needs to be said about the diesel locomotives: medium length trains use a *Class 67* of 3,200hp (2.4MW), weighing 90 tonnes, and shorter trains an ex-HST power car of 2,200hp (1.7MW), weighing 70 tonnes. Assuming there is a sensible rolling programme of electrification for inter-city routes there will be little application for big passenger diesel locomotives and it is probably not worth the cost of developing or adapting such a design.

Plate 11: *The Class 67 diesel locomotives introduced in 1999 have a top speed of 125 mph, and with 3,200 hp installed power are suitable for hauling short or medium length trains (or longer ones in pairs). Some have been allocated as standby locomotives in strategic locations to rescue failed trains or to haul electric trains over non-electrified diversionary routes, such as this one waiting at Newcastle Central.*

For hauling shorter trains, the recently re-engined HST power cars will perform admirably until they are worn out completely, by which time the strategic choice between further electrification and using a modern medium-power diesel locomotive should be clear. After thirty years of operating experience and good standards of maintenance, reliability should not be an issue.

In the few cases where long trains need to be diesel-hauled for a few years, the best solution might be to use pairs of ex-HST power cars, coupled back-to-back, as a sort of 4,400hp (3.4MW) Bo-Bo-Bo-Bo locomotive. This gives the flexibility to split them to power two shorter trains sometimes, rather than being lumbered with a single high-powered diesel locomotive having rather specific applications. In the long term, all inter-city routes justifying long trains would be electrified anyway.

The articulated groups of three coaches are estimated at 70 tonnes per 'triplet'; more on that subject later. Using four bogies, or eight axles, the average axle load is about 9 tonnes. Each triplet is 50m long and will have an average capacity of around 100 seats (e.g. eighty standard class and twenty-two first class seats in a composite triplet). In a long train, perhaps a third of one of the triplets is a buffet or restaurant car. A train may be composed of one to six triplets, plus the locomotive and a driving trailer.

For adequate crashworthiness when being propelled at 150mph, and for sufficient adhesion to assist the locomotive with regenerative braking, the driving trailer is designed to have a weight of 60 tonnes. This gives an axle load of 15 tonnes, the same as the electric locomotive. It is 20m long.

The weights, lengths, capacities and power to weight ratios of the different train formations possible are summarised in Table 1. There is a high degree of flexibility to choose solutions for widely different situations using the same components. Train formations can be altered according to the demands of route topography, commercial speed, service frequency and capacity variations.

Long trains are unlikely to be powered by single ex-HST power cars for normal services as acceleration is low, but they are included in the table for completeness. Such formations may be adequate when trains are diverted to fairly flat non-electrified routes during engineering work.

The power to weight ratios shown in the table are simply nominal installed power (hp) divided by total train weight (t) to give a rough idea of possible performance:

No. of triplets	Seats	Length m	Electric weight	P/W	Diesel Cl.67 weight	P/W	Diesel HST PC weight	P/W
1	100	90	220	27.3	220	14.5	200	11
2	200	140	290	20.7	290	11	270	8.1
3	300	190	360	16.7	360	8.9	340	6.5
4	400	240	430	14	430	7.4	410	5.4
5	500	290	500	12	500	6.4	480	4.6
6	600	340	570	10.5	570	5.6	550	4

Table 1

Train capacities, lengths, weights and power to weight ratios.

Power to weight ratio figures greater than a conventional two-plus-nine HST are highlighted in green. Consequently, all the corresponding train formations can be expected to accelerate better than an HST, and in the case of the shorter electrically-hauled versions very much better.

Adhesive weights for acceleration and braking

Acceleration of a train is not just a matter of power to weight ratio, however. Adhesion will limit the power that can be used to accelerate through the interface between the wheels and rails. The same also applies to braking, which can be thought of as 'negative power' extracting the kinetic energy of the train and converting it into other forms of energy: heat for disc brakes and electricity for regenerative braking.

In the proposed train concept the locomotive provides the acceleration, apart from additional boost power from the driving trailer under certain circumstances. The level of acceleration possible thus depends primarily on the adhesive weight of the locomotive (which has all axles driven) in proportion to the total train weight. This applies particularly at low speeds, where ample power is available to apply high acceleration forces if adhesion would permit them. Needless to say, the percentage of adhesive weight for acceleration varies according to train length and locomotive type.

For braking, all parts of the train have disc brakes and thus the adhesive weight for deceleration would appear to be 100% of the total train weight. This is certainly true at lower speeds where the disc brakes have full effect. At higher speeds, however, the concept recovers some of the train's kinetic energy using regenerative braking, so the percentage of adhesive weight for deceleration then depends on the weight of the vehicles that provide that form of braking. In the proposed concept, only the electric locomotive and the driving trailer provide regenerative braking, and this facility is not available on the diesel locomotives.

Table 2 shows the percentages of total train weights available for acceleration and regenerative braking for the various possible formations and locomotives:

No. of triplets	Electric accel.		reg. brk.		Diesel Cl.67 accel.		reg. brk.		Diesel HST PC accel.		reg. brk.	
	t	%	t	%	t	%	t	%	t	%	t	%
1	90	41	150	68	90	41	60	27	70	35	60	30
2	90	31	150	51	90	31	60	21	70	26	60	22
3	90	25	150	42	90	25	60	17	70	21	60	18
4	90	21	150	35	90	21	60	14	70	17	60	15
5	90	18	150	30	90	18	60	12	70	15	60	12
6	90	16	150	26	90	16	60	11	70	13	60	11

Table 2

Adhesive weights for acceleration and regenerative braking,

and percentages of total train weights.

Considering first acceleration, the adhesive weight percentages give an idea of the possible performance when limited by poor adhesion conditions. The degree of acceleration possible varies inversely with the total train weight, as the maximum traction forces that can be applied are fixed by the level of adhesion multiplied by the adhesive weight of the locomotive.

For diesel haulage, both the *Class 67* and ex-HST power car are rather heavy in relation to the maximum traction forces they can provide. After some energy is extracted for hotel power, the acceleration forces they can supply are roughly one-half or one-third respectively of the capability of the electric locomotive. Of course, these are established locomotive designs anyway, so there is no problem with adhesion there.

In the case of the proposed electric locomotive, the weight is the same as a *Class 67* but the power (and hence the potential traction force) is twice as great. In fact, the situation is very similar to a *Class 91* electric locomotive, which has the same installed power and a slightly lower weight (84 tonnes). The *Class 91* works successfully, with good adhesion performance using individual control systems on its traction motors plus Doppler radar speed detection.

As the proposed electric locomotive is a six-axle design, the acceleration forces on each wheel will be two-thirds of a *Class 91*. That in itself does not help the adhesion situation very much as axle loads are also reduced to slightly over two-thirds of the older design. It does, however, give more scope for detecting incipient slips via more axles and with good design should improve adhesion performance further. Hopefully the technology of motor control has advanced in the last twenty years, allowing this higher performance to be realised.

For higher speeds, the traction forces are much reduced, being inversely proportional to speed as the maximum power is fixed. There should therefore be no problem with adhesion at the higher speeds. At low speeds, it should be possible to have at least as good acceleration as the *Class 91*, and probably quite a bit better. Given all these factors it seems reasonable to suppose that all the electric train formations will have adequate adhesion to cope with the available power.

The overall conclusion to be drawn regarding acceleration is that all possible train formations have adequate adhesion; consequently the power to weight ratio figures in Table 1 do give a realistic view of the performances achievable.

It can be seen that the shorter electrically-hauled formations could accelerate like a rocket from a stop, but it is not desirable to do so. This is a sober, dignified, safe, comfortable Rolls-Royce-driven-by-an-experienced-chauffeur sort of train, not a macho-boy-racer-in-a-sports-car type, trying to impress by giving an exciting ride! Acceleration should gradually increase from a stop for a few seconds, up to a moderate level which is then sustained up to the highest speed possible until the constant power curve kicks in. This will reduce the number of spilt drinks and old ladies falling over as they try to stow their luggage, while climbing up the speed / time graph rapidly to maximise the distance travelled and give high average speeds. The electric locomotive knows automatically what its trailing load is (see Chapter 10), so it can adjust its acceleration profile (in combination with the skill of the driver) to give the optimum results for any train formation.

Braking is a lot more complicated to calculate. At high speeds regenerative braking is used, which is subject to the adhesive weight percentages of Table 2. At lower speeds, disc brakes throughout the train are the dominant effect, acting via the adhesive weight of the whole train. There is no sudden switch between these two methods of braking, however; regenerative braking has full effect at the highest speeds and dwindles to near zero at low speed, whereas disc brakes are little used at the highest speeds and are blended in gradually to have maximum effect at low speeds.

The speed and level at which disc brakes start to be used will vary according to the train formation and locomotive type, the braking rates required, and the level of adhesion. Adhesion levels possible will depend on rail conditions, together with the performance of the speed control systems in the electric locomotive and driving trailer, plus the characteristics of the disc brakes. Braking from 150mph due to adverse signals allows for a gradually increasing deceleration with the doubled stopping distance of the strategy. Deceleration for route characteristics can be a choice between faster schedules or greater energy saving.

Consequently, this is a classic case of system engineering where many factors affect many other factors, and several iterations around the possibilities need to be done before the optimum solutions can be specified. A number of key characteristics can be mentioned, though.

For diesel haulage of the longest trains, the driving trailer has only 11% of the train weight for adhesion, so it will not help braking very much. Its primary purpose in this situation is to store sufficient energy (over several stops) to provide hotel power in the event of the locomotive being uncoupled or breaking down. Consequently, energy recovery is low and the train disc brakes have to cope with most of the burden of braking from 125mph; just like *Mark 3* (HST) coach brakes in fact.

However, there will seldom be diesel haulage of long trains anyway, so these constraints are of little consequence. A more typical diesel-hauled train of two triplets has over 25% of the weight in the driving trailer, so it can recover more energy, the disc brakes start to work at lower speeds and their wear is reduced for the more frequent stopping pattern such a train is likely to have.

The longest electrically-hauled trains manage over 25% of train weight for regenerative braking, mostly in the locomotive. Consequently, a moderate percentage of energy can be recovered during a stop, and wear on the disc brakes reduced somewhat. Such a train would be used primarily for long non-stop high speed runs between main centres, so the number of stops will be low and the daily wear on brakes will be low anyway. For such a train by far the greatest proportion of energy used will be expended in overcoming air resistance, so the amount that could theoretically be recovered in braking makes little difference to the overall energy consumption. As a result, the relatively modest performance of energy recovery in this context is of little importance in the overall calculation of energy efficiency.

Nevertheless, in the critical speed range decelerating from 150mph to 125mph, regenerative braking together with vehicle and air resistance provide about 80% of the total braking force, allowing conventional '125mph' standard disc brake designs on the coaches to cope with their modest 20% contribution at this higher speed. As speed reduces and the deceleration level increases, the disc brakes bear a greater share of the burden; over 60% at 75mph, for example. The level of energy recovery for the longest electric train braking to a stop from 150mph due to adverse signals would need to be simulated in detail to calculate, but at a guess it might be around 40% or so. This moderate level has the advantage of keeping regenerated current levels to the same maximum values which apply on maximum power for acceleration. Consequently these should be manageable on the electrical distribution system designed to accept regenerated power. Also, the level provides ample energy for hotel power while limiting battery capacity in the driving trailer, to be described later. At the same time, disc brake wear should be substantially reduced. Overall, it is a balanced compromise that would not work so well if energy recovery were more efficient.

A typical electric train of four triplets (such as might be used on the Midland main line) has 35% of the total train weight available for regenerative braking. This allows reasonably good recovery of energy and greater reduction of disc brake wear, appropriate to the speed restrictions and medium-distance stops of such a route.

The shortest possible electric train (such as might be used during the night) has a massive 68% of total train weight available for regenerative braking. It can thus provide a high level of energy recovery, giving an efficient solution for the low demand and frequent stops of such a duty.

It is worth remembering that the kinetic energy of a train varies according to the square of its speed. Consequently, a train travelling at 150mph has four times the kinetic energy compared with running at 75mph. In very simple terms, if regenerative braking only is used to slow a train from 150 to 75mph and disc brakes only to slow it from 75mph to a stop, the regenerative braking can recover three-quarters of the kinetic energy. In fact, of course, some disc braking is used above 75mph and some regenerative braking below 75mph, so the efficiency of energy recovery is not easy to calculate.

The performance characteristics of the various train components plus the deceleration profiles all come into the overall calculation too. Nevertheless, it should be clear that the energy recovery performance will be significantly better than a simplistic linear interpretation of adhesive weight percentages would indicate at first sight.

Of course, the various systems are designed to give the braking performance required, so by definition adhesion is sufficient for braking. The simulations need to be done to explore the options in detail, but intuitively *Mk. 3* standards of brakes on the coaches will be sufficient even for a maximum speed of 150mph when combined with the other elements of the strategy.

Overall, the adhesion situation for all possible train formations is perfectly satisfactory, and the coaches only need to have conventional wheel-mounted disc brakes. The level of energy recovery varies according to train formation, but is appropriate to the context in which a particular configuration is used. Good overall energy efficiency is possible for all train formations relative to the theoretical limits achievable under appropriate operating conditions.

High speed running

For diesel haulage, the maximum speed is 125mph and this is the familiar design speed for both the *Class 67* and the ex-HST power car, operating in well known territory. But what happens with the electric locomotive accelerating up to 150mph?

The weight of the longest electrically-hauled train is 570 tonnes. This compares with the 500 tonnes of a standard East Coast formation with a *Class 91*, nine *Mk. 4* coaches and a DVT. The proposed electric locomotive has the same installed power as a *Class 91*, so at lower speeds the acceleration of the new train will be about 12% smaller if the drive system is no more efficient.

As speed increases, there are changes in the relative importance of the various components of force taking up the power exerted by the locomotive. The frictional resistance of the train remains relatively constant. On a flat route, there is no force component increasing the potential energy of the train. At lower speeds, the majority of force exerted accelerates the train. Air resistance increases in proportion to the square of the speed, and is of little significance at lower speeds.

When the maximum power output is reached, the total force available diminishes in proportion to speed so acceleration reduces. Air resistance also starts to absorb most of the force as speed increases. When maximum speed is reached, acceleration has fallen to zero and the dominant destination for the power is in overcoming air resistance, perhaps consuming 75% of the total energy.

The *Class 91* was designed for a top speed of 140mph, so twenty years ago British Rail thought 6,000hp was enough to go at that speed. Since the laws of physics have not changed since then (although many other laws have!), it seems reasonable to assume that a power about 15% greater would be needed for 150mph, as this is the ratio of speed increase squared. The new train is a bit longer than a current *Class 91* formation, but the dominant air resistance at 150mph is probably shifting air at the front end and coping with vortices at the back end of the train, so train length will make little difference. In theory, then, about 6,900hp would be needed for 150mph.

Looking at a *Class 91*, however, it does not seem to be a particularly aerodynamic shape. Research suggests that a tapering profile for a streamlined front end suitable for 150mph should increase gradually over a length of five metres or more. In combination with attention to streamlining near ground level in the whole train, to reduce the vortices caused by bogies, wheels and other underfloor components, it appears that air resistance can be reduced significantly at such speeds. Although the situation needs to be verified, probably the new train would be able to go at 150mph using only the 6,000hp proposed if full attention is given to the aerodynamic profiles of the whole train.

Assuming this works out as expected, a maximum length new train would have slightly less acceleration than a *Class 91* East Coast formation at lower speeds, comparable at medium speeds, and better at higher speeds. It would gracefully accelerate beyond 125mph to 150mph, at a low rate but still useful for long non-stop runs. The headline speed of 150mph looks perfectly manageable if the route is sufficiently straight and flat.

Naturally, the shorter electric train formations will accelerate faster at low and medium speeds, but when 150mph is approached the air resistance at the front and back ends of the train will become the dominant forces and these do not vary with train length. Consequently, the high speed acceleration profiles of all kinds of electrically-hauled trains will be similar. The general appearance of the locomotive will be something like *Figure 7*.

Of course, simulations and prototype trials of the new train will be needed to establish the impact on journey times, but some sparkling performances should be possible by current standards. Since a typical length (four triplet) electric train has the same 14hp/tonne power to weight ratio as a two-plus-five HST formation but also has better streamlining, a higher design speed and less constrained maximum power, it should easily outperform such a train. A two-plus-five HST formation was used in the special demonstration train for the '*Tees-Tyne Pullman*' which reached 144mph in 1985, running from Newcastle to King's Cross in two hours and twenty minutes.

Fastest journey times from London using the new train of two-and-a-quarter hours to Newcastle, three-and-a-half hours to Edinburgh, one-and-three-quarter hours to Sheffield and one hour to Bristol should be perfectly feasible as examples of the kind of performance achievable using the existing route topography, plus electrification where required.

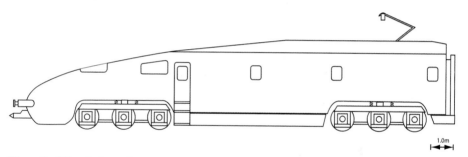

Figure 7: *150 mph electric locomotive.*

Chapter 7

Energy management in the driving trailer

The driving trailer performs multiple functions: assisting the locomotive with regenerative braking; recycling that energy via a battery to provide hotel power to the train; acting as a centre for train information; giving accommodation for staff, luggage and bicycles; backing up refreshment facilities; offering options for shunting, boosting traction and rescuing failed locomotives; and containing the driving cab for use when the train is propelled. In traditional railway terms it can be considered to be a combined brake van, luggage van, guards' van, micro-buffet car, auto-trailer, banking engine and shunting engine!

It does not quite deserve the title of 'locomotive', though; there is no fuel 'input' to provide traction 'output'. Rather, the driving trailer is a recycler of the train's kinetic or potential energy for re-use in other ways; either electricity for hotel power or mechanical force to provide additional, limited, traction. The four axles of the vehicle are connected via drive systems to motors used as generators, which provide current to an energy management system. This in turn charges high capacity batteries in the driving trailer.

The driving trailer weighs 60 tonnes compared with the 90 tonnes of the electric locomotive, and axle loads of both vehicles are the same at 15 tonnes. Adhesion limits the braking forces that can be applied in proportion to the axle load, in other words the same for each axle on the locomotive or driving trailer. No regenerative braking is provided on the coaches. Consequently, the driving trailer can recover 40% of the regenerative braking energy of the electrically-hauled train, whatever its length, and the locomotive, 60%.

The batteries need to have sufficient capacity to absorb the energy generated by a stop from 150mph in a full-length (maximum weight) train. However, regenerative braking works best at high speeds, and friction (disc) brakes take over at lower speeds. As explained above, a long train has only moderate energy recovery performance due to adhesion considerations. So for the maximum length electric train, perhaps about 40% of the train's kinetic energy can be recovered when braking from 150mph.

Energy conversion will be perhaps 80% efficient, considering the losses in the motors, drives and power conversion circuits. As mentioned above, the driving trailer gets about 40% of the available kinetic energy to deal with. Consequently, the batteries in the driving trailer end up storing 0.4 x 0.8 x 0.4 = 0.128 or about 13% of the kinetic energy of the train at each stop from 150mph.

The full-length train weighs 570 tonnes, so at 150mph (67m/s) the kinetic energy is:

$$\tfrac{1}{2} MV^2 = 0.5 \times 570,000 \times (67)^2 = 1280 \text{ MJ} = 355\text{kWh}$$

Consequently, at each stop of a full-length train from 150mph the batteries need to store 0.13 x 355 = 46kWh.

The experimental *Hayabusa HST* was equipped with lithium ion batteries of 48kWh capacity, the same as those apparently required by this proposed strategy. It seems, however, that battery life is optimised for charge levels between about 20% and 60%, although the technology is improving. Consequently, it is probably a good plan to fit 100kWh of battery capacity in the driving trailer. This can absorb the energy of a full-length train stopping from 150mph within the preferred operating parameters, with plenty of headroom. Currently the batteries are supplied as 1kWh modules weighing 20kg, so the battery weight proposed is 2 tonnes. This can easily be accommodated within the design weight of 60 tonnes; the driving trailer will need ballasting anyway so some of that weight might as well do something useful.

Now the discharging of the batteries is considered. In common with all the rest of the train, the driving trailer will be connected to the 'hotel power' electricity bus which supplies the train lighting, air-conditioning, hand dryers, sockets for laptops and shavers, information displays, etc. This is where most of the energy will go: if the batteries are charged to a sufficient level, they are used to power the train lighting and air-conditioning, relieving the locomotive of these tasks until the battery charge level is reduced.

The load on the 'hotel power' electricity bus will be at a maximum when the air-conditioning is working flat out to provide heating or cooling in extreme temperatures, the other loads being relatively small. For a full-length train this will be around 400kW. Consequently, a 60% charged battery can supply the hotel power for at least nine minutes under worst case conditions, and usually much longer. In most cases the air-conditioning can be switched to a lower level for a period anyway without a noticeable effect, perhaps doubling the battery discharge time to at least eighteen minutes. This is ample time to accommodate a change of locomotive from electric to diesel or vice versa at the boundary of an electrified area, or other changes in train formation resulting in the locomotive being uncoupled.

When a train is split into sections the locomotive powers one section and the driving trailer the other from the time of the split until a new driving trailer and new locomotive are attached to the separate parts to continue their journeys. Naturally, if a train is split in the middle, for example, the hotel power load which has to be supplied by the driving trailer temporarily is approximately halved, doubling the battery discharge time. In practice, therefore, battery capacity is sufficient for dealing with changes of train formation.

Since changing locomotives or train formations will be infrequent, there is plenty of opportunity for the batteries to be charged to a suitable level by accumulating energy over many stops, descending gradients or periods of deceleration. The energy management system operates to keep charging the batteries during braking up to a threshold level depending on the current speed. This is to provide sufficient headroom to absorb the energy resulting from a stop from that speed without over-charging. When the threshold is reached, the batteries start to provide hotel power until they have been discharged to another appropriate level. If a train is changing formation then of course it will be stopped, so there will always be at least some charge in the batteries from the energy retrieved recently in braking to that stop.

After the batteries have been charged to the 60% level and start to provide hotel power, the time for them to be discharged again to their original (20%) level depends on the hotel bus loading. For a maximum length train the loading might vary between about 40kW and 400kW, giving a period of battery supply roughly between six minutes and one hour. For typical operating situations this amounts to 'free' (recycled) hotel power for a substantial proportion of the time.

Of course, the time taken to the next charging cycle depends on the train accelerating after a stop or speed restriction and then decelerating again, or restraining speed on a descending gradient. This period will usually be tens of minutes even if stations are fairly closely spaced, and if lower speeds are reached before braking there will be a lower level of charging. It is expected, therefore, that under most operating circumstances all the energy recovered by regenerative braking in the driving trailer will be efficiently recycled into hotel power without the need to dissipate a surplus. The significant proportion of 'free' recovered energy should also encourage generous levels of fresh air flow in the air-conditioning, and discourage the skimping on this parameter which has been a cause of stuffy and smelly environments on some trains in the past.

High levels of air flow should not be noisy though; good design and layout can achieve a fresh but quiet passenger environment.

In addition to providing hotel power under normal operating conditions, there is also the thorny question of how long the air-conditioning must be kept going in the case of major breakdown, such as failure of the locomotive or electric power supply. This facility, not available on current trains, becomes a straight cost issue between the period the rules require the function to be maintained and the provision of adequate energy storage or generation capacity to provide it somewhere on the train. It is easy to be talked into the rather absurd position of having to provide a standby diesel generator on an electric train to solve the problem.

The preferred strategy here is simply to increase the battery capacity in the driving trailer up to the level required by the rules. From a design point of view there is ample capacity for at least ten tonnes of batteries providing 500kWh of storage, which would allow the air-conditioning to keep going for at least an hour-and-a-half from a 60% charge at the half power level on a full-length train. The cost effectiveness of such an approach can be questioned, but increasing the battery capacity also has more useful benefits in terms of providing additional traction capability.

If it is decided that it is essential to keep the air-conditioning active for an hour or two if the locomotive fails, emergency ventilation cannot be arranged, large batteries are too expensive and a standby diesel generator is the only solution; it should be placed on the driving trailer to keep its noise, pollution and vibration away from the coaches and to facilitate maintenance. Hopefully that complication should not be necessary, though.

Assuming common sense prevails and two tonnes of batteries are enough, it would be reasonable to use up to about 30kWh of the battery capacity for traction purposes in the driving trailer. This will be ample for shunting itself and a few coaches to and from sidings when changing train formations: a bit like a *Class 08* diesel shunter used on maximum power for seven minutes. Such a power level might not seem much, but at low speeds little energy is needed except when accelerating or climbing gradients. It should even be sufficient to get a failed full-length train over the crest of a modest hill before coasting down the other side to the next station.

At higher speeds, the traction capacity available from the driving trailer would be sufficient to provide a power boost for a minute or two to overcome a local adhesion problem, or to improve acceleration when a train is running late.

Since adhesion percentages for regenerative braking improve as train formations get shorter, the batteries are charged quite well even for short trains, whereas hotel power loads decrease linearly with train length. Consequently, energy efficiency improves and 'free' hotel power is available for more of the time. On diesel-powered trains with a 125mph maximum speed this effect is countered somewhat due to the lower efficiency of braking from a lower speed, but such trains will typically be shorter and reasonably efficient anyway.

With short diesel-powered trains the battery capacity becomes a much higher proportion of the train's overall energy demands. This has two beneficial effects. Firstly, the locomotive can be relieved from providing hotel power during acceleration, diverting more power for traction purposes. Secondly, there is still sufficient stored energy for boost traction from the driving trailer when accelerating, which improves acceleration over the figures that would be expected in Table 1; just what is needed for the frequent stops of such trains.

Sometimes the energy management system may decide that the charge level is too high for the batteries to absorb all the energy from the next stop, the hotel power load is too low to discharge them to a suitable level quickly enough, and there is no demand for traction power from the driving trailer. In this case the energy management system arranges for the surplus energy to be discharged into an electrical resistance to bring the battery charge level to a more suitable value. The same resistance is used to dissipate the energy from regenerative braking in the event of battery failure or a disconnection from the hotel power bus.

Although rechargeable battery development sometimes seems painfully slow (it is now fifty years since a lead acid battery-powered multiple unit train was tried out successfully in the Aberdeen area by British Railways), battery costs and energy densities are gradually improving. Partly stimulated by the need for better electric road vehicles, some new battery approaches using nanotechnology methods are now being researched. It seems reasonable to suppose that battery technology will improve significantly over the forty-year lifetime of the proposed new train. Consequently, costs will reduce, and performance can improve by replacing the batteries in the driving trailer with new battery technology at the appropriate time.

A proposed design for the driving trailer is shown in *Figure 8*.

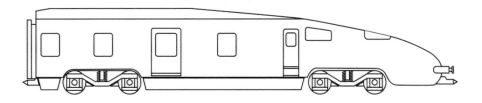

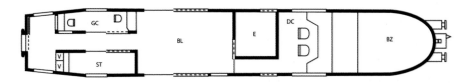

Figure 8: *Driving trailer.*   *GC guards' compartment BL bicycles and luggage storage*
ST storage E energy management equipment
V drinks and snacks vending machines
DC driving cab BZ ballast zone (mostly sand)

Chapter 8

Coach design

Design concept

The coaches could be conventional single units of 23m or 26m length, but this approach has significant disadvantages. As is well known, the British loading gauge is restricted compared to most other countries where the railway network was developed later. Consequently, conventional coaches designed for use on the British network have smaller internal widths and heights than equivalent coaches in most of Europe and North America, and they feel (and are) less spacious.

A further factor to be considered is the increasing average size of passengers, both in height and width, and the requirements of those at the top ends of the size distribution curves. A casual observation of any well-loaded British inter-city train will reveal significant numbers of people wedged uncomfortably into seats between armrests, having knees touching the seat back in front of them, stretching their legs down aisles or ducking to avoid low door openings.

Although it is commendable to provide accommodation for disabled people such as wheelchair users, many more passengers (or potential passengers) are not provided for adequately at present due to lack of space. A few extra inches would make all the difference between 'unpleasant' and 'comfortable' travelling conditions for especially large or tall people. The demographic trends are still towards increasing size, so it is necessary to consider what the situation will be in forty years time as well as now to produce a good coach design for its expected service life.

Extra space is also desirable in the aisles of trains. Staff pushing catering trolleys, passengers finding storage for big cases with wheels, guards checking tickets, parents carrying babies and bags, people walking in opposite directions squeezing past each other and many other everyday movements would be eased significantly with even a little extra space in the aisles.

Wider seating and a wider aisle can be achieved in a conventional British coach body by having two-plus-one seating, using an off-centre aisle with two seats on one side and one on the other. This is common practice for first class accommodation, but for standard class the loss of 25% capacity compared with the usual two-plus-two arrangement is too significant to be acceptable commercially. In order to give sufficient space for a reasonable aisle with two comfortable wide seats on either side, the coach body needs to be as wide as practical.

Since the limit on coach width is partly caused by the need to avoid structures and adjacent trains on curves, a long coach needs to be narrower than a short one as its overhang is greater. Alternatively, the long coach can be restricted to lines with only large radius curves or additional clearance, in which case it can be wider. Neither alternative is very attractive for the long coach, with either comfort or operational flexibility being compromised.

A short coach, on the other hand, has little overhang on curves and can be made wider. It also has extensive route availability, partly because cheaply constructed lines with sharp curves were often designed in the era of short coaches. Although inter-city

Plate 12: *The rear of this train departing from Havenstreet station on the Isle of Wight Steam Railway illustrates the body profile and small dimensions of the traditional British coach, typical of designs from the late nineteenth century when many secondary lines were built. By the 1960s the usual body width was a slightly larger 9 ft 3 in (2.82m) for vehicles of similar length. Note also that the buffers and couplings are slightly above platform level, a position they still occupy today.*

routes have few such constraints, it is a great advantage for the rolling stock to be able to traverse any route for diversions or excursions, or if it is desired to restore through services to some less populated locations through the once common practice of splitting trains.

The solution to these issues is to use the concept of articulation. This permanently couples coach sections together in groups, with bogies near the pivot points and near the ends of the groups. If there are N coach sections, there will be N+1 bogies in an articulated group, rather than the 2N bogies of conventional separate coaches.

Traditionally the idea has been used mostly to reduce costs for suburban trains and trams, where bodies are lightweight and the increased axle loads resulting from the reduced number of bogies can be tolerated. There are advantages for high speed trains too, however, if coach lengths are reduced to bring axle loads down again to appropriate levels. With restricted and suitably damped movement between the articulated sections, stability is better compared to separate coaches able to move freely relative to each other. Articulation is one of the key foundations of the TGV high speed train and its derivatives such as *Eurostar.*

Plate 13: *Although many railways round the world use the same track gauge as in Britain, most are far more generous in their permitted sizes of vehicles. This nineteenth century French double deck coach, seen at the Cité du Train museum in Mulhouse, is too big to fit through many British bridges and tunnels. The optimum technical solutions for British trains are different from those used elsewhere because of these constraints.*

Coach layout

The proposed strategy divides the passenger accommodation of a full-length train into six parts, each part being an articulated group 50m long. Three coach sections are used in the group to make a 'triplet', which runs on four bogies.

If the same sections were designed as conventional coaches, there would be six bogies. Consequently, the weight of two bogies can be saved using the triplet approach, reducing the cost of bogies by a third. In addition, four sets of couplings and all the associated air and electrical connectors are saved by having the three coach bodies permanently coupled together in the triplet.

If a greater degree of articulation were used, the benefits would be less pronounced, however. For example, six coach bodies articulated together would run on seven bogies, compared with eight bogies for two triplets; a reduction of an eighth. Also, two sets of couplings and connectors could be saved. This is not worth the significant reduction in flexibility to match capacity to demand which would result. Overall, the triplet configuration is considered to be the best compromise between cost and flexibility.

Within each coach body there are five modules of standard class seating or four modules of first class. The face-to-face seating module size is 2.1m in standard class,

Plate 14: *The basic idea of articulation for rail vehicles has been around for a century. A single bogie supports the ends of two coach bodies, instead of having a separate bogie for each vehicle. This junction between two Eurostar coaches, seen at London St Pancras International, illustrates the principle.*

with first class around 2.6m. Although the coach body structures are identical regardless of the accommodation, different window panels are fitted (with five or four windows) according to class so that all seats have a good view.

These modules are bigger than the 1.93m standard class and 2.18m first class provided in the original 1970s *Mark 3* (including HST) coaches, before intensive use of closely-spaced face-to-back airline seating to cram in more passengers became prevalent. Spacing is also greater than the 1.9m standard class and 2.13m first class provided for face-to-face seating in the *Mark 4* design. The proposed module sizes are not considered extravagant, however, as the requirement is to accommodate not only taller passengers comfortably but also larger items of luggage between the seatbacks. They also allow a bit more space for thicker upholstery, to get away from the hard inflexible minimalist seats that have become common in many new and refurbished coaches.

Some people do prefer airline-style seating, in place of conventional face-to-face seats around a table. In standard class a typical layout is three modules of facing seats in the centre, with a module of airline-style seats at each end. Placing the airline seats

Plate 15: *A more recent articulation technique is to have some vehicle bodies without wheels at all, instead suspending them from adjacent units. The idea is well established in light rail vehicles, as illustrated by this tram in Valencia. Only the first, third and fifth vehicle bodies have wheels below them, the second and fourth ones being supported by their neighbours on either side. A similar method, on a larger scale, is proposed for coaches in this strategy.*

at the ends puts them near the luggage racks and doors, easing access to them for the infirm, shy or sleepy.

There are substantial luggage racks at both ends of the seating area, on both sides of the coach, about 0.8m wide. These will tend to be filled up earliest with larger items of luggage as they are the first storage spaces encountered when boarding the train. The lowest shelf has the greatest clearance so that the biggest and heaviest items are stored low down, with the higher shelves for lighter items. Fairly large items can be stored between the seat backs in conventional fashion. In addition, there are the usual overhead racks above the seating areas for lighter items.

The windows are reasonably large to give a good view, especially desirable for enjoying the many scenic routes. It is important not to place the bottom of the window too high up in the coach body: this can be frustrating for very young passengers who are not tall enough to see out well when sitting. The height and placing of a *Voyager* window is about right; a rare example of a modern coach feature which is a real improvement on the *Mark 3* design.

Entrance vestibules are about 1.2m wide, similar to the *Mark 3* coach. This allows enough space to deal with big suitcases, pushchairs, etc. Since the seating areas are short, the nearest access doors are no more than seven metres away from any seat, reducing anxiety for infrequent travellers encumbered with luggage. Each seating area contains no more than forty passengers, and has access at both ends. This reduces the potential for tangles between people realising they need to get out at a late stage and those struggling with luggage to find their seats.

The single leaf sliding doors giving access to the train are about 1m wide. They slide into pockets behind the luggage racks, so opening speed can be rapid; in contrast to plug-type doors that need to move outwards before sliding. To avoid the need for grooves in the coach floor, each sliding door is suspended from a double-edged rail near the ceiling and supported horizontally by rollers bearing on both sides near the bottom of the pocket entrance.

Toilets are located at either end of the articulated group, on the opposite sides of the entrance vestibules from the seating areas. At one end, two standard toilets are fitted, one on each side of the corridor. The other end has one larger toilet which can be accessed by wheelchair users, plus seats outside it for the infirm to sit while waiting for the toilet to become vacant, or for the companions of a wheelchair user occupying the free space at the end of the coach. All toilets are equipped with traditional frosted glass windows to give some natural light and to be less daunting to the claustrophobic who hate entering small windowless spaces.

Since the toilets are beyond the bogie pivots, their width will reduce in a taper towards the end of the vehicle to provide clearance on curves, but there is sufficient space anyway. The maximum width areas of the coaches are allocated to seating. The toilets are gravity-fed from water tanks above them, and discharged into retention tanks below them at the outer ends of the coaches. The two standard toilets share common water and retention tanks. Since the toilets of adjacent coaches are nearby, this eases the logistics of filling and discharging tanks at depots.

Since all seating areas are separated from entrance vestibules by luggage racks with two full-height vertical partitions on either side, draughts from open doors at stops should not be a problem and it is considered that internal doors are unnecessary. This removes a major obstacle to boarding and alighting when loaded with luggage. The success of this approach will depend on special care being taken to produce low ambient noise levels in the vestibules, however, from such sources as external airflow, door mechanisms, suspension movements, wheel flats, rattling equipment, creaking and scraping corridor connections, etc. If done well, there should be no difference between noise levels in the vestibules and seating areas when the train is on the move.

Corridor connections at the ends of the articulated group are fairly conventional, with a 0.8m internal width comparable to a standard domestic door opening.

The corridors and aisles between facing luggage racks and toilets are also designed to this width for easy access by catering trolleys through the train.

Articulation and coach width

The pivot points of articulation are at the junctions of the coach bodies, slightly nearer the centre of the group than the nearby bogie pivots. The centre coach body is supported by the outer bodies. On a minimum radius curve, taken as 80m or four chains, the angular displacement of adjacent coach bodies is ten degrees off centre. Consequently the outside edges of the 0.8m corridor at the join between coach bodies are displaced by a maximum of 7cm from the normal position when negotiating the sharpest curves.

The corridor connection here consists of an inflated rubber tube secured at the sides and top to both coaches. The articulation does not allow vertical or horizontal movement of the two coach bodies relative to each other at the pivot point near the centre of the corridor floor, and relative movement near the roof is limited by springs and controlled by dampers. The corridor connection is designed to accommodate these limited movements by compressing on one side and inflating on the other without rubbing on any surfaces. Consequently, its operation should be silent. At floor level, the articulation joint is covered by a resilient floor pad capable of being compressed to the appropriate levels. This is an alternative to the conventional tram or bendy bus arrangement, where the arc of the junction between the two coach floors would intrude into either the luggage or vestibule areas.

In the proposed design the bogie centres are 14m apart, compared to 16m on *Mark 3* or *Mark 4* coaches or 19m on a 26m long design such as SET. This might not seem much difference, but overhang on curves increases rapidly as the distance between bogie centres gets bigger. Taking the minimum radius curve of 80m again, the proposed design has an overhang of 0.61m compared with 0.8m for the *Mk. 3* and *Mk. 4* coaches or 1.17m for a 26m design. The overhang is the maximum displacement sideways of the centre of the coach body from the centre line of the track on a curve, halfway between the bogie pivots.

The consequence of this overhang is that if the limitation on coach width were caused by the need to avoid obstacles such as bridge piers on a minimum radius curve, the proposed design could be (0.8 – 0.61) x 2 = 0.38m wider than a *Mk. 3* coach able to traverse the same route. In other words, the coach could be 3.12m wide instead of 2.74m.

In fact, the situation is not as simple as that: the allowable width depends on a variety of infrastructure profiles on straight as well as curved routes, inherited from many historic railway companies having different standards. A 3.12m wide coach (10ft 3in) would be achievable on the ex-Great Western main lines as designs wider than this operated there 120 years ago; the Midland main line will be a different matter. So the achievable width in practice depends on picking the optimum balance between comfort and route availability, and possibly spending a little money to ease particular infrastructure pinch points. Some previous tight clearances on the inter-city network have already been eased over the last couple of decades.

As a guess, probably a 3.0m wide body (9ft 10in) would be achievable with wide route availability, a little more than the traditional 9ft 3in once common for coaches up to 20m long. The widths mentioned here are at seating (waist) level where space is most needed; there will be a slight narrowing towards the roof to accommodate suspension dynamics and track superelevation, but not to the extent necessitated by a tilting train. Also, the coach body will become narrower below the waist to provide clearance when approaching platform level, accommodating the tolerances of track position and dynamic movement relative to platform edges.

This estimated 9.5% increase in coach width compared with the *Mk. 3* is not large, but helps towards the provision of wider seats and/or aisles. In standard class, each seat could be about 6.5cm (2½in) wider if the aisle were the same as before. Alternatively, 5cm (2in) wider seats could be chosen with a 6cm (2½in) wider aisle. First class seats could be 8.7cm (3½in) wider, as the aisle is wide enough with the two-plus-one seating arrangement used in that case.

Lowering floors for easier access

As well as increasing the width of the coach, the proposed design increases the floor-to-ceiling height of the interior. This is done for two reasons; to give increased headroom for tall people, and to permit level access from platforms. The roof height from rail level remains the same as the *Mk. 3* design, as this is fixed by infrastructure such as tunnels. Instead, the internal height is increased by lowering the floor to platform level.

Although the history of railways in Britain has bequeathed an unfortunately restricted loading gauge, it has also given a helpful legacy of high platforms. Although there are a few examples remaining of lower height platforms, the majority of stations still in use were built or modified in the Victorian era to have platform heights about 0.9m above rail level. In spite of this, inter-city trains have significantly higher floors about 1.2m above rail level, necessitating a step up into the train still. This is primarily done for reasons of convenience, allowing clearance between the top of the wheels and the underside of a flat coach underframe which supports the floor.

This difference in coach floor and platform height is a significant disadvantage. Ramps have to be provided to permit the loading and unloading of catering trolleys and to give access for passengers in wheelchairs. Sometimes on curved platforms where the track is aligned for high speeds there is a big step up into the train, which can be difficult for the infirm. Loading of heavy luggage requires a lift up, which takes time, especially for infrequent travellers unfamiliar with the railway environment. Toddlers have to be lifted into the train, and the gaps between train steps and platform edges occasionally provide opportunities for dropped items to end up on the track where they are difficult to retrieve. It would be much better to have level access with platforms and coach floors at the same height. Even those few stations having lower platforms would have greatly improved access, and recent ideas of adding supplementary platforms to such places for safety reasons would become unnecessary.

Naturally lowering the coach floor reduces the space for under-floor equipment, and at the speeds required it is probably impractical to have the very small wheels needed to fit under a conventional design with adequate clearance. Instead, it is assumed that the optimum wheel size will have the top edge of the flange approximately level with the coach floor. Consequently, there must be holes in the underframe and floor, sufficiently large to accommodate all wheel movements including curvature and dynamic vertical and horizontal oscillations under worst case conditions. This can be done in a way that is invisible from the coach interior.

The proposed coach design uses the conventional approach of outside axleboxes on the bogies, so that there is only a simple axle between the wheels and no other equipment in that area. This gives maximum vertical clearance in the centre of the coach, to accommodate the underframe beneath the corridor.

Considering the horizontal direction, the five degree angular displacement of the bogie on a minimum radius curve will produce a 0.11m sideways movement of the axle, and the outer edge of the wheel will move about 0.15m towards the centre. Allowing for the necessary dynamic tolerances, this permits a low floor 0.8m wide in the centre of the coach to avoid the maximum displacement of the inner wheel flanges.

In the vertical direction, the top of the axle will be about 0.5m above rail level and the top of the underframe supporting the floor will be approximately 0.9m above rail level. The distance between the two of 0.4m is divided between the underframe depth in the vicinity of the axle and the clearance required for vertical dynamic movement. For example, a 20cm deep underframe would allow clearance of 20cm vertically upwards from the nominal position, or 40cm peak-to-peak up and down movement.

The same design parameters mean that the top edge of the wheel flange must be allowed to move up to 20cm above floor level in the worst case. Allowing for a robust metal box to enclose each wheel, this gives a vertical protrusion into the coach interior about 30cm high and 1.2m long, from the corridor towards the coach side. In the proposed design, these wheel boxes form the base of the luggage rack, are below

Plate 16: *Most railways round the world have continued with the low platforms used in the mid nineteenth century. Consequently it is necessary to climb up into the coaches. This Swiss coach, being prepared at Lausanne for a journey to Basel, illustrates a typical entrance, with three steps up from platform level to the coach floor. Such climbs are difficult for the infirm and disabled, and cause delay when loading luggage. They may also represent a trip hazard inside the coach due to the step recess.*

the cabinet for the washbasin in the toilet, or lie beneath the seats outside the disabled toilet. Consequently, they are not noticeable from the inside, and a low flat floor can be maintained throughout the coach in all corridors, toilets and seating areas.

Of course, this narrowing of the coach underframe in the area of the wheels does reduce its structural strength, but the layout allows for strong vertical supports extending from the wheel box areas to roof level. Since the strength of the coach body depends on the structure as a whole and not just the underframe, this arrangement permits a robust, stable design to be maintained.

These vertical supports also provide strength adjacent to the door openings in the vestibules. They are quite wide, and have a box-like structure for low weight. Their interior provides a suitable floor-to-ceiling route for cables, pipes, air-conditioning ducts and the like.

Since the coach body sections are some 30cm wider and taller than a conventional design, and have at most 80% of the length, the tube-like body structure will have inherently greater rigidity. This might allow some weight savings in the choice of materials to compensate for the slightly greater cross-section of the body. In any case, the 70 tonne

Plate 17: *In Britain a standard high platform was adopted by the late nineteenth century, requiring less of a climb to enter coaches. There are still steps up into most British coaches, however, as shown by this HST at London Paddington welcoming passengers on a service to Penzance. An inviting gap under the step provides an easy route to the track for accidentally dropped umbrellas, handbags and teddy bears. The proposed strategy eliminates these issues, providing level access with only a small gap.*

weight target for the triplet should be readily achievable using aluminium construction, as it is the same as two steel-bodied *Mark 3* coaches of similar length. Probably it is worth building a steel-bodied prototype triplet as well to see what weight could be achieved and to assess the relative merits of the aluminium and steel approaches.

The shorter coach body does not necessarily imply a higher resonance frequency with less capability for damping vertical impulses than a conventional design. The body sections are coupled together directly (not via a bogie) so the mass of the adjacent vehicle comes into the picture as well. Careful attention to suspension parameters and weight distribution should provide a smooth ride on less-than-ideal track.

At the side of the coach, the wheel boxes are left open to provide a wheel arch in the same manner as a road vehicle. This provides easy access to the wheels, brakes and suspension for maintenance, and gives clearance for the wheels and upper parts of the bogies when they move outwards on curves. Alternatively, streamlining considerations might result in the covering of these spaces, with only the lower edges of the wheels protruding to reduce air resistance.

Plate 18: *This view of a partly dismantled power bogie, seen at the Eastleigh Works Open Day, gives an impression of the size and mounting of railway wheels. It is possible to lower coach floors significantly if the design allows the upper parts of the wheels to protrude above floor level, restricting the floor to the centre of the coach only in this area. The proposed strategy uses this technique, with the wheels concealed under luggage racks, seats or cabinets in a similar manner to the normal practice on low floor buses.*

Coach doors are placed centrally above the bogies, so that there are no large gaps between the door and platform edge on sharp curves. There is no need for retractable steps: the step edge (level with the coach floor) approaches the platform edges as closely as track position tolerances and dynamic clearances will permit. Even with a modest gap, the level access is a vast improvement on the current situation.

The lower floor will permit access doors about 2m high (6ft 6in), compared to the 1.8m of a *Mark 3* coach. This is the same as a standard British domestic door opening, so only a small number of exceptionally tall people will need to duck to enter the train and even for them the situation is no different from negotiating an ordinary home. Within the train, a minimum ceiling height of 2.1m is proposed in all areas including corridors and toilets: there is still another 0.7m or so of headroom in the centre of the coach to accommodate such things as water tanks.

Within the seating areas, the normal ceiling height would be 2.3m above floor level. This still permits sufficient ceiling space for air-conditioning ducts and an air circulation layout similar to the *Mark 3* coach, avoiding the need for the compact ceiling-mounted air-conditioning units with high noise levels which are an unfortunate feature of some new train designs.

The combination of level access, large and fast opening doors, more even spacing of doors through the train, limited numbers of seats in each area and no internal doors will give greater speed and less hassle alighting and boarding at stations for this design compared to a conventional inter-city train. Although the time spent at stations is most critical for a stopping train, a limited stop train can also benefit from fast access by giving less potential for station delays.

The suggested layout of a typical composite triplet is shown in *Figure 9*.

To give an impression of the increased spaciousness of the design, and to clarify how the wheels fit within the coach structure, a cross-section of the coach is shown in *Figure 10*. For comparison this is contrasted with the cross-section of the *Mark 3* coach as used in the HST.

A suggested buffet / restaurant car triplet layout is shown in *Figure 11*. Since the centre door will be used primarily by staff for loading supplies, it is moved adjacent to the kitchen door in the central coach. This is also convenient for the storage area of a catering trolley just inside the kitchen door. Should a wheelchair user require a full meal, there is sufficient space beside the table to the left of the restaurant car entrance vestibule. A table extension would be fitted in this case. No seats are provided in the buffet car; it is purely a serving bar counter and most passengers will return to their seats in the train. There is sufficient space for standing and chatting in the buffet area too.

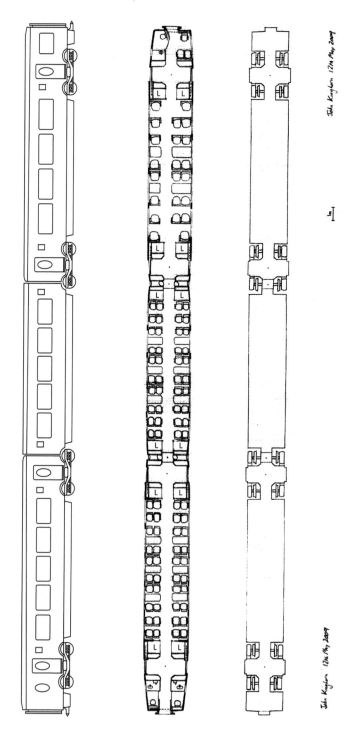

Figure 9: *Inter city composite coach triplet*
L luggage rack

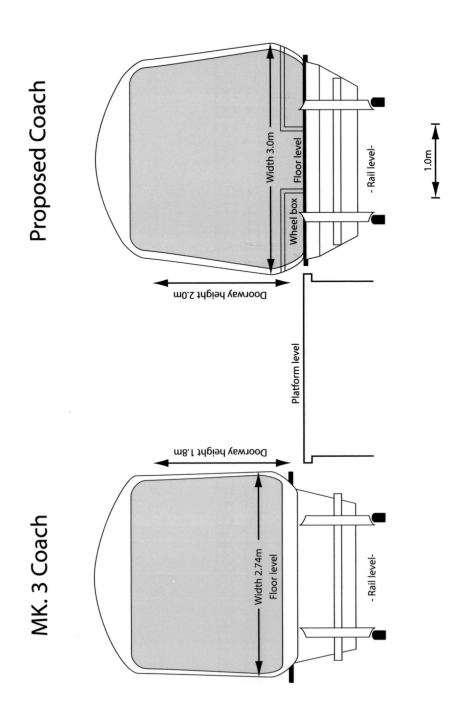

Figure 10: *Cross-sections of Mk.3 and proposed coaches*
Yellow shaded area: internal space in seating area

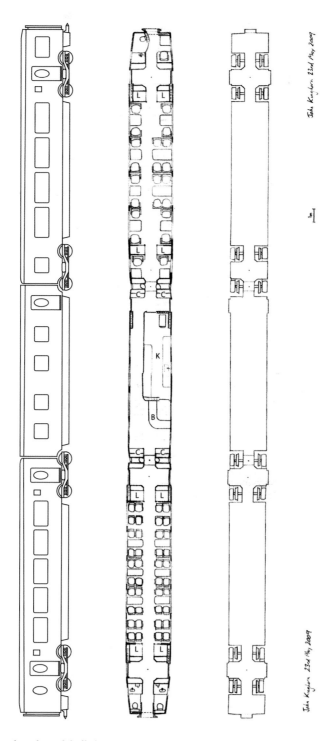

Figure 11: *Coach triplet with buffet/restaurant car*
L luggage rack   C cupboard B buffet counter K kitchen

Chapter 9

Couplings

The streamlined ends of the locomotive and driving trailer at the outer ends of the train are equipped with conventional buffers, couplings and control interfaces. This is to allow the whole train to be rescued in case of breakdown, or to be hauled or propelled by a diesel locomotive on a non-electrified diversionary route when it is desired to retain the electric locomotive to continue the journey later.

Since the *Class 66* freight engine will be the most common diesel locomotive type out on the network for many years, the multiple control interfaces at the ends of the new train are made compatible with that design, as well as the *Class 67* passenger engine. This allows a locomotive to couple up to the rear of a train, which then can still be driven from the leading train cab, without the need for any 'wrong line' working. Only the drawhook is provided on the new train as it is assumed that the three link coupling will be available on the other vehicle. Air pipes and connectors are normally concealed within a compartment behind the streamlining of the new train.

The conventional couplings at the outer ends of the train also give the flexibility to connect to freight vehicles and locomotives, allowing them to be rescued by this train as well as the other way round. Of course in these circumstances speeds will be limited and loads may be abnormal, but the facility might be useful on rare occasions to recover from infrastructure problems such as rock falls on the track or road vehicles damaging rail bridges.

It is even possible to add a freight vehicle or two as a 'tail load' to the train as was once done with diesel multiple units hauling vans. With the current railway organisation structure such 'mixed' trains can hardly be envisaged, but future generations of managers might want to restore such a facility.

Within the train itself, however, a new design of coupling is needed. One reason is that the new lower floor is at the same level as a conventional coupler, and it is not desirable to have a slope upwards at the coach ends just to be compatible with that coupling standard. Keeping a common low floor level throughout the train is preferred

Plate 19: *Since 1988 the Class 66 diesels have become Britain's ubiquitous freight locomotives, with nearly 400 in service for many operators. Consequently there is a reasonable chance of finding one of these engines nearby if a passenger train breaks down, or of some being available at weekends to haul electric trains over non-electrified diversionary routes. The proposed long distance train has compatible couplings and control systems at its outer ends, to allow the Class 66 to come to the rescue easily when necessary.*

to avoid slopes for catering trolleys and wheelchairs, so the couplings between the coaches need to be lower to avoid the floor.

This necessity for a change anyway provides an opportunity to rethink the requirements for a coupler in the context of this flexible train strategy. It should not be necessary to have staff at track level to perform the tasks required for coupling and uncoupling coaches; all these should be performed automatically by commands from the driver. The situation is a bit more complex than joining or separating sections of a multiple unit train, however; this train can be divided at any point between the coach triplets and there are no driving cabs in the vicinity to define where the split should be. In addition, the corridor connections at the dividing point need to be closed off before the two sections are separated, and it needs to be clear to passengers where the split is so that they can be reassured that they are in the right part of the train.

Dividing trains works as follows. Before arrival at the station where the train is to be divided, announcements are made and displays activated to indicate the calling points of each section. Different announcements can be directed to different coach groups so that it is clear which part is going where. On arrival, a member of staff (for

Plate 20: *Interfaces between vehicles can become rather complex, especially if different standards and methods of traction have to be taken into account. This Class 73 electro-diesel locomotive on display at Eastleigh shows the old way of doing things, with an array of jumper cables, brake pipes and control connectors to be seen as well as the couplings and buffers. Most of these had to be dealt with manually, with the shunter in a rather dangerous position for coupling and uncoupling operations.*

example, the guard joining the front section) boards the train and closes the manual sliding doors which block off the corridor connection at the splitting point, one door for each coach. These doors can be locked in either the open or closed positions from either the inside or outside: when open they almost disappear into a pocket behind the toilet so are hardly noticeable. The staff member is also present in the right area to reassure any confused passengers and sort out any muddles of families being split up etc.

When both of these doors are closed and locked, an electrical interlock permits the couplings below those doors to uncouple when commanded to do so. Before that can be done, the driver and the guard at either end of the train must agree that uncoupling can take place, so both authorise the command when unloading is complete, the train doors have been closed and the train is still stationary. The command electrically activates valves to release the couplings, powered by air pressure from the coach reservoirs, then the locomotive or driving trailer can ease forwards or backwards to split the train.

Once split, a driving trailer (moving under its own power) can be attached to one section of the train and a locomotive to the other. Coupling is effected automatically by shunting up to the coaches. Once coupled together, members of staff (usually the

Plate 21: *More modern couplings have all the functions grouped together, with automatic control from the cab and no need for a member of staff on the track. This Class 508 electric multiple unit on show at the Eastleigh Works Open Day illustrates the concept, with a coupler for traction and braking forces and a shrouded connector beneath it. A similar idea is used in the proposed strategy, but with a new standard design having enhanced facilities for more flexible train formations and mounted well down on the vehicle to be underneath the new lower floor level.*

guards) can unlock and open the manual doors to restore access, locking them in the open position. In this normal state, uncoupling is impossible even if commands are sent inadvertently. The locomotive also has a corridor connection, to facilitate transfer of staff on the move.

The couplings are designed to cover all the interfaces needed between vehicles in one standard format. They are robust enough to withstand traction and propelling forces on the heaviest trains, with maximum levels of acceleration and braking, on the most uneven track. They include compressed air pipes for the train brakes and pneumatically activated functions such as sliding doors and the couplings themselves. They have facilities for multiple locomotive controls in conventional fashion. They contain the 'hotel power' electrical bus which drives the main facilities such as air-conditioning. They have a high bandwidth passenger services bus, for such functions as satellite to wi-fi wireless router internet facilities. They provide facilities for driver-to-guard communication, control of the train doors, passenger announcements and display information. They have provision for video feeds from security cameras and the train movement cameras referred to earlier. Finally, they include the train information bus, to be described below.

The mechanism of the couplings provides for all connections to be shuttered when vehicles are uncoupled, to prevent the ingress of snow, rain and debris. On coupling, the shutters are opened immediately the symmetrical plug-and-socket guide members of the couplings start to engage, before further movement causes the electrical and air connections to be made. When coupling is complete, the locking catches spring into position and this same action causes the air pipes to be opened and a contactor to connect up the hotel power bus.

When uncoupling, a successful command opens the locking catches by air pressure from the coach reservoirs, at the same time closing the air pipes and opening the hotel bus contactors. In this way, uncoupling takes place when the high power lines are already disabled. All these functions are integral to the coupling design, so there is no need for further isolating equipment in the coaches.

A further function of the coupler is to provide an electrical signal that is activated as soon as the couplings start to engage (before any connections are made) and ceases when coupling is complete and the latches are locked successfully. When uncoupling, this signal is activated from the receipt of an 'uncouple' command until the couplers are fully disengaged. When the signal is active, fast-acting circuits in the locomotive and driving trailer disconnect the hotel power bus. When the signal disappears, the locomotive reconnects the hotel power bus. The driving trailer, however, waits for a second or two to sense whether the hotel power bus is powered by a locomotive or not, and only if power is not present does it start to provide hotel power itself.

A separate signal is sent from the driving trailer to the locomotive when the driving trailer seeks to provide hotel power in the situations described previously. Again, the driving trailer waits until it detects that power has been switched off from the locomotive before starting to provide power itself. Similarly, when the locomotive has had its hotel power generation switched off, it waits for authorisation from the driving trailer or the prompt from the uncoupling signal and checks that power is not present before switching on again.

The arrangement prevents conflicts in power generation and the time delay gives the locomotive priority over the driving trailer when sections are coupled together. During coupling and uncoupling there will be short discontinuities in the supply of hotel power while the train facilities work out what should provide power where. These discontinuities should only be for a few seconds, however, and although air-conditioning will stop briefly train lighting (especially of the LED variety) can be arranged to keep going for that period. Equipment such as train displays will usually have large capacitors in their power supplies so that they can tolerate such gaps too, and laptops and mobile phone chargers connected to the train sockets will not mind either. It is assumed that single phase AC will be the most economical method to distribute hotel power.

The only need for rechargeable batteries in the coaches is to power a small number of emergency lights, the audio information system and the 'black box' of the train information bus to cover the very rare occasions when there is a complete failure of hotel power in traffic. These batteries are all of a low capacity.

The streamlined ends of the locomotive and driving trailer are also equipped with couplers to the new standard, below the conventional couplers. This facilitates shunting of coaches by either of these two vehicles from either end.

Chapter 10

Train information bus

Since train formations are fully flexible, it is necessary for the train control systems to keep track of which vehicles are present at any time for many purposes, for example to arrange seat reservations. In addition, it is desirable to have some degree of status monitoring of the vehicles so that any faults are discovered early and logs of performance can be generated automatically. These functions and others are provided by the train information bus.

Each coach group or other vehicle (including the locomotive and driving trailer) contains a small 'black box', supplied by the hotel power bus and containing a small rechargeable battery which can maintain its function in the absence of power. The black box stores fixed information about the vehicle and receives signals from various sensors in the vehicle. It also has outputs to control various functions.

The black boxes are connected together by the train information bus, which has serial data in a standardised format, via dedicated connectors on the couplers. Data can be received and transmitted through the train information bus in both directions, with the black boxes acting as 'slaves' to commands from either the locomotive or driving trailer. The interconnection of black boxes is a 'daisy chain' configuration, with the train information bus passing 'through' each black box on its way from one end of the vehicle to the other.

Each black box relays the information received on one bus connection by retransmitting it on the other, and adds its own information to the serial data stream. In this way, the data collected at either end of the train becomes a full picture of all the vehicles in the train. The order of the vehicles is defined, and even which way round the vehicles are can be determined as each black box adds slightly different data according to which direction the information is passing through it. A diagram of the concept is shown in *Figure 12*.

Fixed data provided by the black box is stored in ROM (Read Only Memory). This includes a description of the vehicle (e.g. composite coach triplet), its number, its

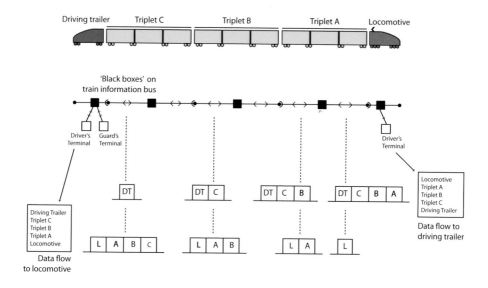

Figure 12: *Train information bus*

manufacturer, its weight, its facilities (e.g. twenty-two first class and eighty-two standard class seats, two standard toilets and one wheelchair access toilet), its maximum speed, its sensors and its controllers.

Variable data provided by sensors connected to the black box could include status of coach doors, status of corridor doors, presence of hotel power, status of lights, health of air-conditioning, saloon temperature, liquid level in tanks, etc.

Outputs from the black box include audio to loudspeakers, feeds to internal displays, feeds to external destination displays, feeds to seat reservation displays, lights and air-conditioning controls, door control disables for selective door opening at short platforms, etc. Vehicles can be addressed individually or any combination of groups of vehicles can receive the same data.

The data format is designed to have plenty of space for expansion, so that in future many new functions could be added without the need for additional bus wires. Of course, there would have to be wires between any new sensors and the black box, but the train information bus infrastructure itself would remain unmodified. The temptation to festoon the vehicle with lots of sensors just because it can be done should be resisted, however; each function should be carefully considered in the light of the cost of monitoring it relative to the benefits obtained from doing so.

The black boxes should not be expensive; they consist of a standard single board computer or equivalent plus some interface circuits to provide the especially robust and EMC-tolerant train information bus connections and sensor inputs. Software costs per unit should be moderate, as every black box is more or less the same thing with only a few vehicle-specific parameters programmed into it. No safety-critical functions would be included, and there would be no local controls. No local displays would be provided either, so the black box could be mounted in any convenient position. In or near a vertical support near the doors would be an obvious place, given its duct-like facility for routing cables.

Suitable software in the terminals located in the locomotive and driving trailer can thus gain a comprehensive picture of the train status at any time. This information would also be logged, to help in detecting incipient faults, monitoring train performance and providing pre-event information in case of incident. The guards' compartment in the driving trailer is the main hub for collecting and monitoring all this data; the terminal located there would provide a simple 'all OK' message if parameters were all within defined limits, and alert staff to any abnormalities found. Enquiries via the terminal (or via diagnostic equipment in depots) could provide detailed information about the current status and history of any specific item.

The guard's terminal in the driving trailer also downloads the seat reservation information to the coaches, refreshing the data at termini or whenever there is a change in train formation. The train company's reservation computer would supply the terminal with data via any preferred method: probably the most effective in future would be via the satellite to train link provided primarily for wi-fi internet connection. Then seat reservations could still be updated on the move, so that last-minute changes of plan could be accommodated. For example, an alert message on the guard's terminal might be 'Due to low demand on this bank holiday there will be no Coach M added today, so the few passengers with seat reservations in Coach M have been reallocated seats in Coach J instead'.

The train information bus relays seat reservation details to the displays beside the seats, which retain that data until updated. The black box simply passes on such messages in a standard format; it has no involvement in storing or processing these commands itself.

Within each coach there are also displays indicating the coach number (a letter); since train formations are fully flexible the letter needs to be programmable and there should be no paper labels. This information is downloaded to the appropriate coach via the train information bus. Similarly, outside each coach there are also displays including the coach letter. The temptation to make these displays scroll between coach letter and destination information should be resisted; confusion often reigns on some trains currently when people are trying to find reserved seats and the vital message 'This is Coach D' has vanished! The display should remain static throughout the journey, and a different display (or a different part of the same display) should be used for destination information. As an aside, the external displays should preferably be the reflective LCD type rather than light-generating LED matrices, to be easily readable in bright sunlight (power consumption is much less too).

The destination displays are also driven from the guard's terminal in the driving trailer via the train information bus in the same way.

A similar process transfers digital audio messages to the coaches, either from the guard's handset microphone or pre-recorded messages from the guard's terminal.

Since the driving trailer is the main repository of train information, changes of locomotive from diesel to electric make no difference. Of course there needs to be some coordination when trains are split or combined: a newly added driving trailer needs to know about the existing still valid seat reservations in its section of the train as well as new reservations if potential confusion is to be avoided. This could be done by interrogating the coach displays, or by making sure that the guard's terminal is already pre-loaded with the correct data consistent with that provided by the previous driving trailer.

Although able to access all the train data too, the driver's terminals in the locomotive and driving trailer cab would focus more on the technical train status, calculating total train weight, monitoring the status of power generation, battery charge level, etc. They would primarily provide alerts to any malfunctions or parameters outside limits.

The train information bus is also the mechanism that allows the locomotive to optimise automatically its acceleration, top speed and deceleration profiles according to the load of the vehicles that are currently in the formation, making allowance for any special features a particular vehicle might possess.

Chapter 11

Changing tastes from COCOA to BOVRIL

The design proposal described so far forms the strategy for a new inter-city train on the established network. But hang on a minute; just what *is* an inter-city train?

Traditionally it would be categorised as long-distance, fast, good level of comfort, long journey times over, say, two hours, serving primarily big cities, good facilities such as restaurant and buffet cars, high traffic levels, good revenue generator etc. The passengers would be mostly travelling infrequently, certainly not daily, for business and leisure.

In the established way of thinking, there are several other categories of train too.

First, there is the medium-distance cross-country train, with shorter typical journey times and fewer facilities, but still primarily catering for infrequent travellers on routes with lower traffic densities between medium-sized communities.

Next, there is the local stopping train, traditionally slow and infrequent, maintaining a limited service to smaller towns and rural stations with low traffic densities and a hopeless loss-maker, so it has to be cheap.

Then we have the outer suburban commuter train, with medium-distance journeys for mostly daily travellers; high traffic densities, reasonable average speeds, a captive audience, lower standards of comfort will do, fairly frequent stops so need quick loading and unloading.

For shorter distances there is the inner suburban train for long-suffering big city commuters, many stops so acceleration and fast loading are crucial, top speed capability largely irrelevant, fairly short journeys so OK to make many stand in peak periods, low average speed.

Finally, there is the tube or metro train; high traffic densities, short distances between stops, many doors and level access for speed of loading, many standing passengers throughout the day, very low average speeds.

Because of these different requirements, tradition says, passenger trains have to be designed completely differently according to the role they have to play. Consequently, trains designed for one purpose are unsuitable for another. The philosophy could be called Conventional Optimisation of Coaches for One Application, or COCOA.

COCOA has been around a long time. For example, in the LNER of the 1930s it produced the *Coronation* (inter-city), the *Cambridge Buffet Express* (outer suburban) and the *Quad-art* (inner suburban). In the British Rail era of the 1980s, there was the HST (inter-city), *Class 158* (cross-country) and *Pacer* (stopping).

Other factors have been at work to increase the fragmentation of passenger rolling stock. The plethora of locomotive designs with different multiple working standards, changes from vacuum to air brakes and steam to electric heating in the 1960s reduced the interoperability of rolling stock in locomotive-hauled trains. Diverse approaches to diesel, third rail electric and overhead electric multiple units further reinforced the idea that trains of different kinds were incompatible and could not be coupled together.

This process has continued and even accelerated in recent years. Technical expertise has largely migrated from railway authorities to train manufacturers, who have no commercial interest in making their products compatible with those of their competitors, especially with 'build and maintain' contracts becoming dominant in the privatised railway. Since train procurement is usually treated tactically in the absence of any agreed coherent national technical strategy, deals are done and rolling stock incompatibilities remain, with different standards from different makers. This situation for passenger trains contrasts strongly with the freight sector, where just about any vehicle or group can couple to any other.

At the same time, the market for rail travel has changed markedly over the last half-century and continues to change. A particular factor here has been the growth in long-distance commuting, with fast inter-city services encouraging people to move out of big urban centres and into medium-sized places. Consequently, most inter-city trains now have a significant proportion of regular travellers for at least part of the journey: places like Swindon, Grantham and Kettering spring to mind for commuting to London. Even for short distances, between Bath and Bristol, Newport and Cardiff, Chesterfield and Derby, Wakefield and Leeds or Durham and Newcastle, that inter-city train *is* a commuter train partly.

This trend should be welcomed, not resisted. The dual-purpose nature of the train provides an efficient use of resources, with the short-distance flows in the examples above naturally balancing the reducing long-distance loadings as the train gets further from London. The higher levels of comfort attract more commuters than a purely local train service would, and the inter-city service still has to serve the main centres, so overall it is a better way of providing the capacity than using more local trains.

The idea of multi-purpose trains does not fit comfortably with railway management structures and approaches, though. Especially since the 'sectorisation' of British Rail through to the current plethora of privatised train operating companies, there are strong organisational incentives to compartmentalise the railway business into different types of traffic. This is understandable enough when it comes to financial accountability, especially when some types of business can be 'profitable' and others are heavily subsidised by the taxpayer. It is a convenient way of thinking about the management issues, but it does not fully reflect the reality of the rail business as a whole. Any idea of cross-subsidy might be anathema, but in fact there are many links between the railway businesses and all depend for their success on each other to some extent. A passenger from, say, Harringay to Harrogate does not magically change from a commuter to an inter-city traveller to a local train user during the course of the journey: the railway gets the business because of the facilities offered by the network as a whole. Nevertheless, the established habits of thinking dictate that three different kinds of train are needed for the three parts of the journey in the above example.

The COCOA philosophy has meant that the quality of train service provided to stations throughout the country in the last half-century has been largely a matter of luck, depending on whether the location happened to be on a main line or not. If not, you usually have to make do with a relatively slow, cramped and noisy diesel multiple unit, sorry. Compare the fortunes of York with Lincoln, Darlington with Middlesbrough, Crewe with Wrexham, Swansea with Aberystwyth, etc.

Another consequence of the approach is that the main lines get more and more crowded with traffic, while the secondary lines are often lightly used as services are unattractive, and lack of demand means they do not improve. They could make a much bigger contribution to the transport needs of the country overall with some investment in better rolling stock. If the coaches were economical but comfortable and just the same as those for the main lines, that would help to transform the fortunes of those forgotten places, encourage a modal shift away from cars and facilitate more even economic development.

The national rail strategy (and yes, there should be one!) should avoid the trap of excessive focus on the high profile main lines and new high speed routes, and put sufficient effort into dragging the quality of secondary line services up to a comparable level to the main lines. Many of those routes currently ignored as low demand and not worth investing in can be built up gradually with fast short trains becoming more frequent and then longer as demand increases. The way the Cross-Country and TransPennine businesses have been built up in the last couple of decades provides a model that could be followed in many other places.

Usually markets respond very positively to genuinely improved facilities or performance. The lessons of the past (both positive and negative) should not be forgotten.

Suppose in the 1970s the HST had not been introduced, and inter-city services had remained limited to 100mph maximum speeds with traditional patterns of service provision. What would have happened to the passenger rail business in Britain? One can only speculate, but it is fair to assume that the recent achievement of 1950s passenger volumes again (in spite of vastly increased car use and a reduction in rail network size) would not have been possible. Sensible investment with a clear vision to increase market share transformed inter-city travel positively, and much of today's rail passenger business depends on that legacy. It is even arguable that the HST saved the British railway network as a comprehensive national asset.

On the other hand, lack of investment and insensitivity to the competition inevitably produce decline and collapse. Railway enthusiasts often bemoan the demise of branch line services, and many that would have been valuable today have been lost. It is hardly surprising this happened, though: a look at old railway timetables from the 1950s reveals the sheer awfulness of many services in comparison with the then competing bus services. For many secondary rail services that did survive into the 1970s, the move from an old but comfortable locomotive-hauled train to a slow, noisy and rattling diesel multiple unit with bus-type seats and dodgy heating was not always a positive step, and much business was probably driven away then and never regained.

Half of the population now have no experience of rail travel at all, and regard it as irrelevant to their needs. With increasing awareness of the environmental problems of car travel and many roads being congested, however, there are opportunities for rail to increase its market share significantly. That can only happen through more attractive services, though, and better rolling stock is a significant part of the requirement. Very few people will willingly swap a car for a Pacer, even if the rail journey is faster or car parking difficulties are avoided. Higher standards of comfort are needed to make a real impact; but there is undoubtedly untapped demand in many places if an adequately attractive rail alternative can be offered.

For all these reasons, the proposed strategy seeks to minimise the differences between train designs unless they are absolutely necessary, taking advantage of synergies and economies of scale to raise standards on the network as a whole. The intention is to have a small set of interchangeable components that can be used in many ways to cover all kinds of requirements. Following the good example of the freight sector, any vehicle can be coupled to any other vehicle, and the existing muddle of multiple incompatible coupling standards is abolished.

This fundamental change in design philosophy needs a name to distinguish it from COCOA. Let us call it Broad Optimisation of Vehicles Removing Interoperability Limitations: BOVRIL. Yes, BOVRIL does taste peculiar if you are used to COCOA, but probably in time you will get to like it!

The following chapters describe how vehicles designed according to the BOVRIL approach can cover various different kinds of trains.

Chapter 12

Cross country trains

The category of 'cross country trains' is perhaps rather confusing. Services from Scotland, the North East and North West to the South West and South Coast, branded as 'Cross Country', are properly inter-city trains like any others. They have the same standard inter-city equipment already described, and the core routes are early candidates for electrification, if not already electrified.

Instead, the sort of train services meant here cover medium to long distances on routes with medium traffic densities. Most of them were once in British Rail's not-sure-what-to-call-them-and-not-very-interested-in-them category of Other Provincial Services. Currently, they are operated mostly by diesel multiple units of the *Class 158* or *156* varieties. At present, few of the routes are electrified.

They are a fairly diverse group: current examples include about three-hour journeys from Birmingham to Aberystwyth or Cleethorpes to Manchester Airport, and five hours or more marathons from Liverpool to Norwich or Stranraer to Newcastle. Although many of these trains predominantly serve intermediate stations, there are some through passengers.

There is no good reason why standards of comfort on these cross country routes should be any lower than inter-city journeys taking the same or shorter times. Yes, traffic densities are lower on these routes, but short trains should not mean uncomfortable trains. The strategy achieves a high level of comfort by using exactly the same coaches as the inter-city ones, up to three triplets, and the same driving trailer, powered by an ex-HST diesel power car.

At nearly twice their intended life, the HST power cars' capital cost would have been written off long ago if they had not been re-engined recently. Also, many will become redundant as their inter-city routes become electrified: two are available from every train taken out of service. Consequently, they ought to be relatively cheap to lease until they wear out completely. This provides a golden opportunity

Plate 22: *The Class 156 diesel multiple units introduced in 1988 are well designed, but their limited facilities and top speed of 75 mph mean they are not really suitable for long cross country journeys. This one, seen arriving at Haltwhistle on a service from Newcastle to Stranraer, still has 191 miles and 13 stops to go before it will arrive at its final destination 4¼ hours later, an average speed of 45 mph.*

to test demand by transforming the performance of these cross country services at little financial risk.

The train can go at 125mph where the route permits with regenerative braking help from the driving trailer. Even with the maximum passenger capacity of 300 seats (360 if standard class only) the power to weight ratio is two-thirds of an HST. That is more than the *Class 31* plus six *Mark 1* coaches which would have been used in the 1960s for the same capacity train.

Better still, with the shorter train the adhesive weight of the driving trailer becomes a higher proportion of the total train weight. Consequently, a higher percentage of the train's kinetic energy can be stored on stopping, which can give more of a boost to acceleration from the driving trailer when starting again. With a typical train capacity of 240 standard class seats using two triplets, the combination of power car and driving trailer will give HST-standard acceleration up to medium speeds until the battery runs down again. From that point upwards there is 80% of an HST's power to weight ratio, still pretty good.

86

Plate 23: *The class 158 diesel multiple units, introduced in 1990, were designed for cross country services with a maximum speed of 90 mph. For years they suffered from poor air-conditioning and cramped low seating, but these issues have now been improved. This one waits at Swansea on a service from Gloucester to Milford Haven, a journey of 176 miles taking 4¼ hours with 36 stops, an average of 41 mph.*

Think what that means for the secondary cross country routes: HST levels of acceleration and 125mph top speed, and better than HST levels of comfort. Compare that with the current situation of a *Class 158* going at up to 90mph or a *Class 156* at up to 75mph. The solution is almost bound to attract many more passengers if marketed adequately.

Yes, the coaches are designed for 150mph and they are only used up to 125mph, but is it really possible to save so much money by having a 125mph design instead? Is negotiating the curves and gradients of that cross country route with its more frequent stops and dodgier track really less onerous for the suspension than gliding down a straight main line 25mph faster on a limited-stop train? As for the coach brakes, they *are* 125mph standard brakes; it is only regenerative braking from the high-tech electric locomotive and the driving trailer, together with the signalling strategy, which lets that inter-city train go at 150mph. The rest of the coach design is as simple as it can be for the required level of comfort, and there are economies of scale in manufacturing it to exactly the same design as the inter-city coach.

Plate 24: *A cross country service operates between Cardiff Central and Portsmouth Harbour, the 141 mile journey taking just under 3½ hours with 16 stops, an average of 41 mph. The hourly off peak journeys are typically provided by 3 car diesel multiple units made up from one and a half Class 158s, as in this example leaving Bath Spa station. The proposed cross country train would offer greater speed, spaciousness and capacity in the medium term. In the long term, the logical solution would be electrification of the whole route, with Salisbury as the natural changeover point between overhead AC and third rail DC power supplies.*

Yes, the driving trailer is quite expensive, but its technical capabilities provide high standards of acceleration, economy of fuel consumption and good back-up in case of locomotive failure. It also has the passenger service facilities appropriate to a long-distance train, with refreshments available at low staffing levels and ample capacity for bicycles to enhance its eco-friendly credentials. In common with the coaches, economies of scale in manufacturing the driving trailer to the same design as the inter-city requirement should constrain costs and improve flexibility.

Since the train goes much faster, journey times should be reduced substantially on most cross country routes. Many use main lines for part of the journey, so by going faster the cross country trains will be less in the way of inter-city traffic on those stretches. Shorter journeys mean that fewer trains are needed for the same frequency of service. A whole new era of cross country travel could begin if the opportunities presented by the re-equipment of the main lines are grasped in this way.

Plate 25: *Diesel multiple unit heaven – or is it hell? The Class 159s are three car versions of the Class 158, with a 400 hp diesel engine under each coach. One waits at Salisbury for a few minutes before proceeding to Gillingham on a service from London Waterloo. Another is parked on the right before its next duty, while on the left a Class 158 has arrived on a local service from Romsey. Out of sight on the left, a six car Cass 159 formation waits on a service to London Waterloo. The total of 14 diesel engines idling simultaneously in the station produces an astonishing noise, making it an unpleasant environment for those waiting for even more racket generators to take them to Cardiff or Portsmouth.*

In time, of course, the HST power cars will need replacing, so at that point the choice is between new diesel locomotives, or further electrification and a new lower power electric locomotive design. By that time the success of the new cross country service strategy will be known. Perhaps some routes would not in themselves justify electrification, but can benefit from synergies with other electrifications for freight or inter-city traffic and only need a little extra effort to complete their networks.

Probably some cross country routes will have improved their business sufficiently to justify full inter-city status with long electric trains by 2030 or so: the Liverpool to Cambridge and Norwich route looks a likely candidate, for example.

In the highly unlikely event of this cross country strategy being unsuccessful in attracting sufficient new business, the ex-HST power cars would be scrapped and the coaches and driving trailers reallocated to the inter-city services, so the investment is not wasted. The cross country routes would then revert to the best of the cheaper hand-me-down trains which could be scraped together from elsewhere. This gloomy

Plate 26: *The Class 170 three car diesel multiple units entered service in 1999, a good design with 100 mph capability for medium distance journeys. They do, however, have the usual DMU limitations regarding comfort and capacity. This one is arriving at Leuchars on a service from Aberdeen to Edinburgh Waverley, a journey of 130 miles which takes 2½ hours, an average of 52 mph. Hopefully services such as this can be electrified and operated by proper locomotive hauled long distance trains in the medium term, with significant improvements in speed and comfort.*

scenario is most improbable, though; the transformation in performance will most likely bring about greatly increased rail commuting on the cross country routes in the same way as it did on the main lines over the last two decades. Higher traffic volumes and increased revenue will probably fully justify the higher cost of the rolling stock after a few years, and may make a greater contribution to the cost of maintaining the route infrastructure too.

Plate 27: *Cross country trains hauled by diesel locomotives are now rarities, as the solution is considered to be too expensive. Occasionally, however, older inter-city coaches are pressed into service to cover rolling stock shortages, to the delight of passengers given their higher levels of comfort compared with the usual diesel multiple unit. Such a train waits at Bristol Temple Meads on a service from Taunton to Cardiff Central, comprising four 1970s air-conditioned coaches with a Class 67 diesel at each end for easy reversal.*

91

Chapter 13

Stopping trains

A few stopping trains remain on main lines in combination with faster services, but mostly they are found on low-density routes where they form the only sort of service provided. Although their primary purpose is to provide transport facilities for smaller communities, many have survived because of other factors such as summer flows to the seaside or tourists coming for the ride to enjoy the scenery. In some cases they have a predominantly 'commuter' character, often for school and college students rather than adults going to work. For remoter places they may be lifelines for the community in areas of poor roads and little public transport provision.

Few such services are electrified, unless they share part of their journey with routes electrified for other reasons. Those that are electrified can be treated as 'commuter', to be described later. In general, traffic volumes would not justify electrification, so most stopping trains will remain diesel operated.

Usually the stopping train needs only a rather low capacity, but some of the journeys are long. Currently it takes two-and-a-half hours from Weymouth to Bristol, four hours from Swansea to Shrewsbury and over five hours from Mallaig to Glasgow, for instance. Consequently, high levels of comfort are necessary in these cases, both for 'normal' passengers and to attract the tourists that provide the primary source of revenue, allowing these services to continue as vital links for their local communities.

High speed is not such an issue for these routes; in fact going too fast would reduce their attractiveness as scenic tourist lines. In any case, the curvature and gradients often make high speeds impossible even on long stretches between station stops. On the other hand, quite often these services have parts of their journeys on main lines, so a reasonably high top speed is needed to avoid being a hindrance to other traffic on those sections. In addition, shorter journey times will improve the competitive position of these services for normal passengers in relation to other modes of travel, and most routes do have some opportunities to travel faster. A maximum speed of 100mph is considered appropriate.

Plate 28: *Local stopping trains sometimes operate over rather long rural routes. This one waits to depart from Oban on a West Highland line service to Glasgow, the journey taking over 3¼ hours for the 101 miles with 13 intermediate stops, an average of 31 mph. Away from the ever-popular 'Jacobite' steam train, casual observation suggests that the West Highland lines are much less busy with summer tourists than they used to be in the days of locomotive hauled trains. Did the introduction of diesel multiple units improve the overall finances of these routes as intended?*

Stopping trains do need fairly high levels of acceleration and braking to give acceptable average speeds. This is necessary both to minimise delays from the frequent station stops, and to cope with the many changes of permitted line speed as the train negotiates the curves, bridges, tunnels and elderly track frequently encountered on such routes.

In addition, rather fast access is needed to limit station dwell times. Although the number of passengers is small, the time spent at each stop soon mounts up on through journeys, given the large number of stations. Even an extra fifteen seconds at each stop means ten minutes more for a journey from Carlisle to Lancaster via Whitehaven, for example.

With its low revenue, the stopping train cannot generally justify an expensive locomotive and driving trailer. It can, however, sustain a lower power approach where the functions of locomotive and driving trailer are combined in one vehicle.

This is the strategy proposed for the stopping train. The main passenger accommodation is in one coach triplet, which is the same as the inter-city and cross country

Plate 29: *The single car Class 153 diesel units are used for local stopping services on the least busy routes, which can still have significant numbers of passengers. About 30 people wait patiently for the doors to be released on this example at Lincoln Central, 5 minutes before departure time. Despite having only one coach, there is sufficient capacity for the journey to Peterborough via Sleaford and Spalding, the 57 miles with four intermediate stops taking 1 hour 22 minutes, an average speed of 41 mph. The proposed 100 mph stopping train design would reduce such journey times significantly.*

vehicles already described, with the exception that one standard toilet is replaced by a driving cab. The triplet now contains two toilets, one standard and one with wheelchair access, sufficient for the generally lower traffic levels and shorter average journeys of such a train compared with an inter-city or cross country service. If the accommodation is all standard class, there are 120 seats in the triplet. The high comfort, low density seating, big windows for a good view of the scenery, and level access with wide doors for fast loading are all appropriate features for a stopping train travelling on long journeys, so there is no need to change them.

Since there is no streamlined front end, but a corridor connection at the front like many DMUs or EMUs, the coach speed is limited to 100mph when running with its cab end first. That end also needs to be ballasted slightly to satisfy safety requirements in case of collisions. Other than having the cab and a slightly higher weight, the coach triplet is identical to the design mentioned before. The layout is shown in *Figure 13*.

Since the cab occupies the left hand side, and the corridor and toilet outside it remain, the driver has a good forward and left-hand view but no view to the right. This

94

Plate 30: *There is considerable diesel train working on electrified routes in many parts of the country, which is a pity from the performance, running cost and environmental points of view. A small example is this Class 153 arriving at Lancaster on a service from Morecambe to Preston, a journey of 25 miles which will take 36 minutes, an average of 42 mph. The terminus at Morecambe is less than 3 miles from the main line: electrifying this small gap would allow an improved train service and assist the earnest efforts to revive the fortunes of this once popular seaside resort.*

is solved by a video camera on the right hand side of the vehicle pointing towards the rear; it gives a good view of island platforms on that side via a screen in the driving cab. There is no need for a cab door to the outside: a sliding door gives access to the corridor, and the usual train doors are adjacent.

The single coach triplet is coupled to a diesel power car, which includes the technical functions and accommodation of the locomotive and driving trailer combined on a smaller scale, together with more seating. The power car is 21m long, maintaining the 14m spacing between the bogie centres in a Bo-Bo configuration to give wide route availability, and has the same low floor design as the coaches. It has an underfloor diesel engine with electric transmission, similar to the technology used in a *Voyager* coach. There are driving cabs at both ends, with a similar layout to the cab in the coach triplet. This gives flexibility for the power car to be coupled to the appropriate end of the coaches to give a driving cab at each end of the train.

Within the diesel power car there is a compartment for the energy management equipment, a refreshment vending area, a wheelchair space, a wheelchair-accessible

Plate 31: *The Pacer diesel multiple units are derived from an experiment in the late 1970s to produce a low cost local train based on a standard bus design. They give a reasonable ride on straight continuously welded rails, but the suspension of the four wheel coaches does not work well on jointed track, pointwork or sharp curves. Two Pacers forming a four car unit arrive at Aber near Caerphilly on a Penarth to Bargoed via Cardiff service, a 21 mile journey taking an hour with 13 stops. Although the service is slow, a good frequency is provided with a train every 15 minutes.*

toilet, a medium-sized storage area for bicycles and luggage, and twenty-eight standard class seats. The layout of the diesel power car is shown in *Figure 14*.

The local stopping train for long journeys thus has a total seating capacity of 148, and is 71m long. Unlike a DMU there is only one diesel engine to maintain. In common with a DMU, however, any number of trains can be coupled together, should the need arise for higher capacity or to split trains for different destinations. Most of the seating capacity (81%) is in nice quiet coaches, free from the noise and vibration caused by engines, motors or drives.

A pleasant feature from the first generation DMUs, which later designs omitted, was the forward view through the cab. This aspect is partially re-introduced in the diesel power car: there is an end window on the seating side as well as the driver's side, together with a window in the corridor door. When the corridor connection is in use, the door folds back against this side window rather than sliding. Although the feature can hardly be described as an observation car, some forward (or backward) views are available for passengers in the outer seats, emulating a popular feature of the

96

Plate 32: *The first generation diesel multiple units introduced in the 1950s had many limitations but a nice feature was the good view through the cabs at either end of the train. This photograph of an end compartment of such a train at Leyburn on the Wensleydale Railway shows the ambience, much enjoyed by small boys pretending to be engine drivers and others observing the passing scene. It is proposed to reintroduce a similar facility on the diesel power cars used for local stopping services, enhancing the view for tourists on Britain's many wonderful scenic rail routes.*

Tyne and Wear Metro trains. Since many stopping trains are on highly scenic routes, this should be an attractive improvement not available on current trains. If a service is lightly loaded, the passenger has the choice of a seat with a better view with more noise from the engine in the diesel power car, or a conventional side view seat gliding along in quiet comfort in the triplet.

No guards' compartment is provided in the diesel power car; instead, the guard can occupy an unused driving cab when not moving through the train. All driving cabs are equipped with a terminal that can access all kinds of data about the train derived from the train information bus. Announcements and displays can also be originated from any cab; this would normally be the responsibility of the guard. Since many stopping trains are long distance, seat reservation facilities are available in the same way as the inter-city or cross country train; a terminal in the diesel power car is the repository of that data in place of the driving trailer.

The diesel power car has the same low floor as the coaches with the bogies and wheels accommodated in the same way. Fitting the 750hp diesel engine, alternator and traction motors in the limited space under the floor is rather a squeeze but it should be possible. Like the *Voyager*, there are frame-mounted traction motors and cardan-shaft drives to the wheels. Maximum speed is 100mph.

The total weight of the local stopping train is about 120 tonnes; 45 tonnes for the diesel power car and 75 tonnes for the triplet. This gives a nominal power to weight ratio of 6.25hp/tonne, which might seem a little on the low side for a train that needs high acceleration. However, the diesel power car also carries batteries, which can increase the power to the traction motors.

Since the adhesive weight of the diesel power car is about 37% of the total train weight, and as the braking requirements from a maximum speed of 100mph are much less onerous than they are for the inter-city or cross country train, regenerative braking can be highly efficient. This is just what is needed for a train that spends much of its time accelerating and decelerating for many stops and route constraints. When braking, the traction motors act as generators to charge the batteries, and the stored energy is then used to supplement the diesel engine power for the next acceleration. This produces substantial savings in fuel and disc brake wear, reducing running costs.

Kinetic energy of the 120 tonne train running at 100mph (45m/s) is:

$$\tfrac{1}{2}mv^2 = 0.5 \times 120,000 \times (45)^2 = 121.5 \text{ MJ} = 33.7 \text{kWh}$$

If an efficiency of 80% is assumed for regenerative braking, the batteries are charged by $0.8 \times 33.7 = 27$kWh at each stop from 100mph.

Since this kind of train is more likely to be operating on remote rural routes, it has relatively more resources to cope with the situation if it breaks down, as rescue will often be further away. A suitable size of rechargeable battery would be about 50kWh, half the size of that proposed for the driving trailer of the inter-city train, even though the stopping train has only one-quarter of the capacity. Such a battery will weigh one tonne, well within the capability of the diesel power car. It can keep the lights and air-conditioning going for at least an hour from a 60% charged condition if the diesel engine breaks down, and will have more than sufficient capacity to move the train slowly to the next station, given the relatively close spacing of stations on such routes.

Of course, under typical operating conditions there will be few occasions when 100mph is reached, so on average there will be far less charging of the battery from regenerative braking. This does not matter, though. As the diesel engine, alternator, energy management system and battery are now adjacent in the same vehicle, power transfers can be arranged in a hybrid drive philosophy. So although regenerative braking works in the same way as before to charge the battery when stopping or descending gradients, the battery can be charged by the diesel engine directly as well.

Consequently, the diesel engine only needs to produce the average power required over the period when the battery is charged and discharged. When accelerating strongly, power from the diesel engine goes to the traction motors, and also the battery supplies additional current to the traction motors to improve acceleration.

During a more moderate acceleration, power to the traction motors can be supplied by the diesel engine, with the battery charge level remaining static. Alternatively, traction power can be supplied by the battery only with the diesel engine idling.

When running at a constant speed, the more limited traction power is supplied by the diesel engine and the surplus power charges the battery. For coasting all the diesel engine power can charge the battery, and for braking the battery is charged further from the traction motors used as generators.

The diesel engine is thus run more steadily rather than in conventional stop-go fashion, improving its reliability and fuel efficiency. This is in addition to the energy saving from regenerative braking itself. Acceleration is also significantly improved; exactly how much depends on the route speed profiles and inter-station spacing, but typically the battery might provide half the traction current on accelerating from a stop, temporarily doubling the power available to give a 12hp/tonne style acceleration performance. The higher train capability, especially acceleration but also top speed to a lesser extent, should reduce journey times significantly on stopping train routes.

If desired, it can be arranged that initial acceleration from a stop is provided primarily by battery power, the diesel engine only making its full contribution after moderate speeds have been reached. In addition to giving a smoother acceleration profile, the approach reduces noise and pollution from the diesel engine in stations.

The stopping train concept can be thought of as a modern version of the classic *Southern DEMU* (Diesel Electric Multiple Unit), but with the important difference that the power car is detachable from the coaches. The power car is limited to 100mph but the coaches are not: they can be added to the formation of 125mph cross country trains or 150mph inter-city trains without difficulty. This gives full flexibility to reintroduce through coaches to the most remote destinations if desired.

Yes, the proposed design is probably more expensive than a conventional DMU. Over its lifetime, however, fuel and running cost savings give significant advantages and should change the financial picture completely. On this kind of service most energy will be spent in acceleration and climbing gradients, not lost in air resistance. In this design most of the kinetic and potential energy resulting can be recovered and re-used instead of being thrown away completely in the brakes as it is in a conventional train. Fuel costs should drop significantly. There is one diesel engine to maintain instead of two or three, and the train brakes will have little wear so maintenance costs should drop too.

Also, the more comfortable and faster train should attract higher loadings and generate greater revenue. This is especially true for the 'optional' passengers, the tourists visiting the area or just coming for a scenic ride. Encouraging such business will be critical for many stopping train routes, which need to get reasonable volumes in summer to compensate for rather lean times with few local passengers in winter. A comfortable seat with a good view and at least minimum drinks and snacks availability at all times are necessary facilities to attract the casual tourists to these services.

For shorter distance local stopping trains, such a high standard of comfort is probably unnecessary and higher capacity might be needed. Some of these lines have quite high peak flows of commuters but depend on only one train shuttling up and down their route. In that case, a coach triplet with higher density seating can be coupled to the same diesel power car. Such a triplet is shown in *Figure 15*; it has six modules of seats per coach with a capacity of 144, with wider aisles for additional standing space. Total seating capacity of the train thus rises to 172.

For this kind of service, seat reservations are seldom necessary, so the at-seat displays in the triplet can be dispensed with to save costs. The triplet's 'black box' on the train information bus simply informs any enquiring terminal that seat reservation facilities are not available on these coaches. For flexibility, however, the diesel power cars always have seat reservation displays, so any reservations on a short-distance stopping service can be accommodated there (including those who like to book the 'observation car' end seats!).

The seating capacity of one diesel power car and one coach triplet is quite enough for most of the stopping services envisaged here, but if more capacity is needed then two or more trains can be coupled together. The driving cabs are switched in or out using a key carried by the driver: if a cab is switched out its control signals are routed to the adjacent coupler for use further up the train. As an additional safety feature, a cab cannot be switched in unless the nearby corridor door is locked in the closed position, using the same electrical interlock which permits uncoupling as described earlier.

At the other end of the capacity scale, the diesel power car can run by itself as a single unit railcar with a capacity of twenty-eight seats. This would be suitable for lightly loaded services in remote locations, transporting staff to engineering worksites, etc. With a nominal power to weight ratio of 16hp/tonne and effectively double that with battery assistance, it could scuttle quickly along the most devious route. As well as increasing the popularity of some little-used services by dramatically reducing journey times, the performance of the diesel power car operating alone would be particularly useful in cases of service disruption or emergency. Large numbers of passengers could be conveyed quickly after incidents for short periods as there is significant standing capacity in the corridor, vestibules and cycle storage areas.

Although the combination of one coach triplet and one diesel power car is the standard stopping train configuration, other formations are readily possible. A particularly hilly route with frequent stops needing faster services could have two diesel power cars and one coach triplet. As convenient, the diesel power cars could be coupled together at one end of the train, or one at either end.

Conversely, a train on a flat route with few stops not needing a fast schedule but requiring greater capacity could have one diesel power car and two coach triplets. The power car could be at one end of the train, or even in the middle if the leading coach has a cab at the front end.

Longer trains, for use at peak holiday times or for excursions, can be made up from as many coach triplets and diesel power cars as desired according to the capacity and performance required. This flexibility is also useful for moving rolling stock around the network as needed.

Standard inter-city or cross country coach triplets without driving cabs can also be used for the stopping train, but in this case of course the diesel power car will have to run round the train at the termini to be at the front again in the same way as a conventional locomotive. This will increase turn-round times a little, but for longer distance services that is not usually an issue. Many terminus layouts still have run-round facilities, retained for locomotive-hauled excursions or freight traffic.

As well as standard coach triplets, the diesel power cars can haul sleeping car triplets. This is an appropriate configuration for night services to remoter places; see Chapter 17.

Although at present it is difficult to imagine the revival of a railway parcels business using passenger trains, future generations of planners and managers might be able to achieve it. In that case the diesel power cars are suitable vehicles to transport low numbers of parcels and newspapers to the smaller communities they serve, having a reasonable van space. They could also haul small numbers of vans (designed with suitable couplers) if parcels business outgrows the capacity of the power cars themselves.

The diesel power cars will also be handy vehicles available in smaller places to perform shunting and locomotive duties with other rolling stock when not in service on passenger trains. These could include tasks like hauling a few wagons filled with cleared lineside vegetation, or propelling snow ploughs. They are also appropriate vehicles to investigate infrastructure issues, given the good views from their end windows. For example, after a stormy night the diesel power car can venture out early onto the line with staff to look for fallen trees. It can accelerate well to do the job quickly and can brake rapidly in case of trouble. It can then return to its base to haul the first passenger train of the day: no different vehicle is necessary.

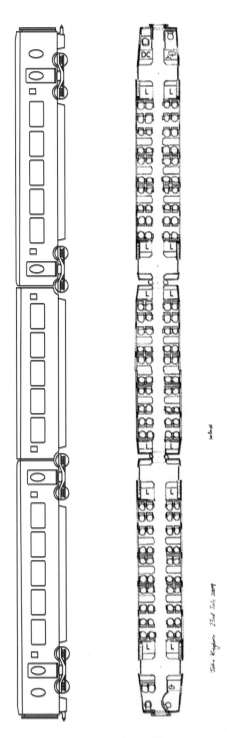

Figure 13: *Stopping train coach triplet (standard class only)*
     L luggage rack DC driving cab

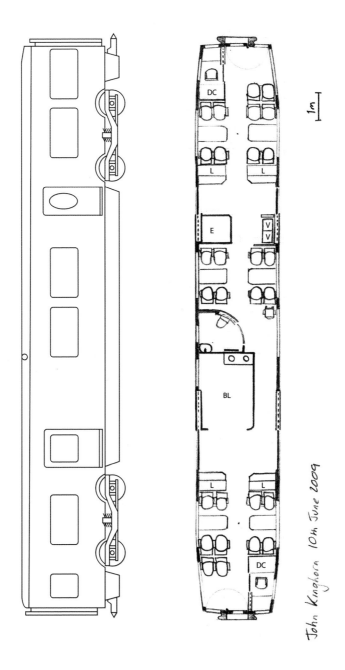

Figure 14: *Stopping train diesel power car*
BL bicycles and luggage storage L luggage rack
E energy management equipment DC driving cab
V drinks and snacks vending machines

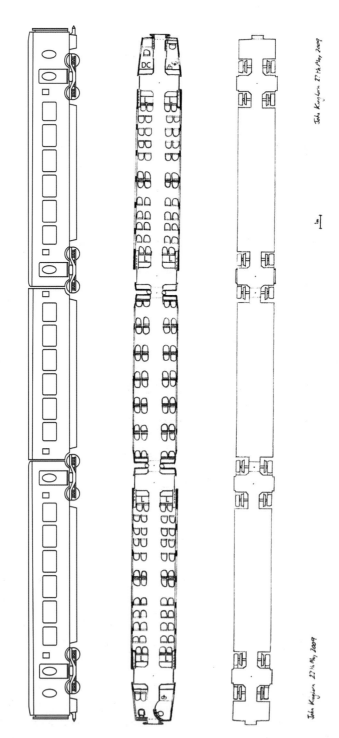

Figure 15: *High density (commuter) stopping train coach triplet*
     L luggage rack   DC driving cab

Chapter 14

Commuter trains

Commuter trains cater primarily for daily travellers to work or college using the same stations, rather than less regular passengers going to different places. As mentioned earlier there is really no clear-cut distinction between commuter and other trains, but some characteristics become more marked as the commuter-like character of a service increases.

A major factor is the variation in density of traffic throughout the day. Since most passengers are going to work, there are very high peaks of traffic in the early morning and early evening, with relatively few travellers in the middle of the day or late evening. This is a significant cost issue, as sufficient numbers of trains are needed to cover the peak loads but far fewer are necessary in off-peak periods. Ideas of discounting tickets to encourage travel at less busy periods may not have much effect, as most passengers need to travel at work times. Consequently, the efficiency of using the resources is low: in off-peak periods trains lie idle in sidings or carry very few passengers in relation to their capacity, and the infrastructure is under-utilised too.

A second factor is the semi-captive nature of the market. At peak times most roads in urban areas are heavily congested, and competing travel methods in cars and buses are slow or unpredictable. Also, many prefer to avoid the hassle of driving under such conditions, especially if car parking is difficult. A significant number of commuters have no access to cars anyway, and many have organised their lives to be dependent on trains for access to work. In many urban and suburban areas, the absence of a commuter rail service would cause the remaining local transport networks to come to a grinding halt at peak periods.

As a result of these factors, attracting more commuters by providing higher standards is usually not high on the agenda of train operators; the passengers will come anyway if conditions are acceptable. Concerns are more about coping with the increasing numbers, by providing higher density seating or more standing room. On the other hand, it is in the interest of operators to encourage off-peak traffic to improve the overall economics of the operation. However, their business depends primarily on the peak traffic, so handling that effectively with the right balance of cost, performance and comfort is important.

The traditional method of handling such commuter traffic is the multiple unit, either diesel or electric. This is particularly advantageous when speeds are low, stations are closely spaced, and high acceleration and braking capabilities are critical requirements. The approach also allows train lengths to be varied (in rather coarse steps) without changing the power to weight ratio, thus making performance consistent and, in theory, permitting standard pattern timetables throughout the day.

The multiple unit approach does have some disadvantages too, however. The restricted capability to reduce train lengths often means that off-peak trains are still lightly loaded in relation to their capacity. More importantly, not only seating capacity but also traction capability lies idle in off-peak periods as sections of trains are discarded.

A locomotive-hauled approach allows a different philosophy to be applied to commuter services. The train performance is designed for maximum capacity peak loads as before, but when coaches are removed in off-peak periods the power to weight ratio increases. This allows faster off-peak services, which should attract more non-commuter traffic, which is valuable in improving the overall economics of the operation. A consequence, of course, is that standardised timetables (a train at xx minutes past the hour) cannot be applied throughout the day: peak and off-peak times will be different. In many cases, however, peak and off-peak times are already different anyway as extra services are introduced at peak periods and station dwell times are increased to cope with the greater numbers of passengers joining and leaving trains then. Using the alternative approach of locomotive haulage, the advantage of higher off-peak performance outweighs the perceived disadvantage of not having day-long standard timetables. Another way of looking at it is to say that there *is* a standard (fast) timetable all day, except in peak periods!

Long-distance commuter trains

As noted earlier there has been a significant growth in long-distance commuting over the past quarter-century on routes that were previously inter-city in character. Consequently for those routes a choice needs to be made between standard train services for both inter-city and commuter traffic, or separating them into two different kinds of train. If the latter course is chosen, long-distance commuter trains will usually share tracks with inter-city trains for all or part of their journeys.

Those routes having sufficient traffic density to justify separate commuter trains will inevitably have rather high service frequencies, especially at peak periods. Because commuter trains also serve the smaller stations, they are likely to get in the way of the inter-city trains. If the speed and acceleration performance of the commuter trains is too low, they are likely to damage the performance of the inter-city trains; ideally they need even higher acceleration and equally good top speed.

The proposed solution for the long-distance commuter train is almost the same as the inter-city train; exactly the same locomotive and driving trailer are used. Costs are reduced, however, by having higher density seating in the coach triplets, using the same kind of layout already seen for the shorter distance stopping train. Most long-distance commuter trains will have reasonable numbers of first class passengers, though, so the accommodation balance is different from the stopping train. In addition, the width of the coaches permits fairly comfortable two-plus-three seating to be introduced in standard class to cope with the numbers, to avoid many standing for long distances as sometimes happens now. The layout proposed in each coach is five modules of two-plus-two seats for first class, or six modules of two-plus-three seats (except at the ends) in standard class. This gives a seating capacity of 40 first class and 118 standard class in a composite triplet, as shown in *Figure 16*.

A maximum length (electrically-hauled) long-distance commuter train with six triplets thus has a capacity of 948 seats; 240 first class and 708 standard class. This is suitable for the heaviest commuter loads, predominantly to and from London. Access is still good enough for such traffic, with 1m wide doors and a maximum of 60 seats in each coach.

Outside peak periods, a typical long-distance commuter train might consist of three triplets with half the above seating capacities. If it is interleaved with inter-city trains of, say, five triplets, the commuter train has a 39% advantage in power to weight ratio, which helps to prevent it delaying the inter-city services. It can still travel at 150mph where the route topography and inter-station spacing permit it.

The biggest timetabling problem for such routes will remain peak periods, and then as usual it is a question of finding creative solutions with different stopping patterns and making use of infrastructure facilities to give the optimum results. Overall, though, the train performance available should allow substantial reductions in journey times compared with current equipment.

In many situations it might be considered that the high density seating described above is not good enough to attract off-peak traffic over long distances. If so, standard inter-city or cross country coach triplets may be substituted in off-peak periods. Where peak loads are not especially high, a good solution might be to mix both types of coach in the train in peak periods, and discard the high density ones outside those times. For example, a train might consist of three low density and three high density triplets at peak times, with a capacity of 774 (186 first class and 588 standard class).

At other times the train would have three low density triplets only, the capacity being a perfectly adequate 306 (66 first class and 240 standard class). Probably only the low density coaches would have seat reservation displays, thus satisfying non-commuter requirements off-peak and making the better seats reservable (at an extra cost?) in peak periods.

For long-distance diesel-hauled commuter trains the same locomotives and driving trailers are used as the inter-city solution, in combination with the same coaches as the electric commuter train. Usually flows will be much lower in diesel areas: if traffic levels increase then generally electrification would be justified sooner or later. A long-distance diesel commuter train from a provincial city might typically have two high density triplets with 252 seats, hauled by an ex-HST power car and the standard driving trailer. Maximum speed is 125mph and nominal power to weight ratio is 8.1hp/tonne, but acceleration is a bit better than this would imply because of boost power from the driving trailer after every stop. On a long-distance commuter route with moderate to long inter-station spacing, the train will give substantially better performance than the existing DMU solution normally used for such traffic.

Quite often traffic levels will be low enough to make high density seating unnecessary: the long-distance commuter train then uses low-density triplets and it becomes indistinguishable from an inter-city or cross country train. Its vehicles can be freely used for any application likely to be encountered in the vicinity of its smaller city or conurbation.

Outer suburban commuter trains

The next sort of commuter train covers medium distances where route topography, inter-station spacing, no inter-city services competing for capacity and/or a fairly captive market determine that 100mph operation is fast enough. This is the kind of service often described as outer suburban; journeys of an hour or so, covering about 40 to 80 miles. In this case the locomotive and driving trailer solution may be considered to be too expensive.

If traffic densities are moderate to high, the traditional approach would be to use a conventional multiple unit, perhaps with four car units that can be run as eight car trains in peak periods. Typically, each unit would have 1,500hp installed power and weigh 160 tonnes, contain about 240 seats and be around 90m long. A maximum capacity train would thus have 480 seats and be 180m long; using currently favoured technology maybe 16 axles would be powered or even all 32 of them.

The proposed concept for the electric outer suburban train takes a different approach. A maximum capacity train runs with four triplets, two powered and two

Plate 33: *Many outer suburban services on AC electrified lines are operated by four car electric multiple units with a top speed of 100 mph. They can be coupled together for greater capacity at peak times, retaining the same power to weight ratio and acceleration, as illustrated by this Class 350 formation loading at London Euston on a service to Tring. The 32 mile journey with 8 intermediate stops will take 46 minutes, an average speed of 41 mph. Although the proposed outer suburban train would have a similar performance at peak times, shorter off peak trains could be significantly faster. Note also the step up into the train, which would be eliminated in the proposed solution with level access.*

unpowered, in any convenient order. The unpowered triplets are the same as the coaches for the stopping train described earlier, with a driving cab at one end. Powered triplets have a driving cab at both ends; they contain a pantograph, transformer and other power equipment in one of the end coaches, which has a guard's compartment and a reasonable cycle space too. Only the four axles of the two bogies in that coach have traction motors, with a total installed power of 1,500hp. The other two bogies are unpowered. As usual, each triplet is 50m long, with the same body structure as other coaches.

A typical outer suburban service will have a modest number of first class passengers in peak periods, but very few outside that time; the proportion will drop as well as the absolute level. So the majority of first class accommodation goes in the unpowered triplets, which are only used in peak periods. The powered triplets have a few first class seats only. Suggested layouts for the unpowered and powered triplets are shown in *Figures 17* and *18* respectively.

Plate 34: *At present many outer suburban services are operated by diesel multiple units, such as this Class 165 formation arriving at Leamington Spa on a London Marylebone to Birmingham Snow Hill service. These trains have a maximum speed of 75 mph, and the 112 mile journey with 7 intermediate stops takes 2¼ hours, an average speed of 50 mph. Services such as this should justify electrification in the medium term; in the meantime the proposed 100 mph diesel stopping train would be suitable, using as many power cars and coach triplets as traffic demands.*

The unpowered triplets will have a weight of about 75 tonnes; because of the traction motors, transformer and electrical equipment the powered triplet is estimated at 85 tonnes. Consequently, a full-length train will weigh about 320 tonnes. It will have 468 seats in total, and will be 200m long. So the full-length train is more or less the same as the conventional EMU solution in terms of capacity and performance (9.4hp/tonne). It could hardly be otherwise if the same technologies and seating density rules are applied.

However, the proposed solution is much more flexible. At 'peak shoulder' times, the train can have two powered triplets and one unpowered one, giving a capacity of 342 seats. The power to weight ratio improves by 30% to 12.2hp/tonne. At this time of day it might be preferable to keep to the same train timings as peak periods, but there is more acceleration in hand to recover from any disruption arising from the most difficult peak period. During the day, trains can run with two powered triplets; seating capacity is now 216 seats, and power to weight ratio has improved by 87% compared with the full-length train to 17.6hp/tonne. That should dramatically speed up off-peak journeys. Finally, in the early morning or late evening, trains can run with one powered triplet by

Plate 35: *Some diesel operated commuter services have more of an inner suburban character with frequent stops, a scenario not ideally suited to conventional diesel traction. An example is this Class 150 three car diesel multiple unit at Worcester Foregate Street waiting to form a service to Dorridge via Birmingham. There are 14 intermediate stops on the journey of 44 miles taking almost 1½ hours, an average of 30 mph. The proposed diesel stopping train could be used for such routes, the hybrid drive technology giving faster acceleration for higher average speeds. In the long term, electrification would be better still.*

itself; the seating capacity is now 108, and the power to weight ratio remains at 17.6hp/tonne to maintain the fast off-peak timings.

A significant technological difference with this concept is that only 25% of the axles of a full-length train are powered, in comparison with the EMU solution using 50% axles powered or all of them. This means eight relatively big traction motors and drives instead of sixteen or thirty-two smaller ones. Potentially this could result in significant savings in capital and maintenance costs, but is the approach satisfactory?

The four powered axles are in the heavier part of the triplet due to the weight of the traction motors, transformer and electrical equipment. The weight of that coach plus half the articulated centre coach produces a load of about 48 tonnes on those four axles. This gives a perfectly acceptable axle load of about 12 tonnes average, maybe 14 tonnes maximum due to uneven weight distribution. The adhesive weight of the eight powered axles in a full-length train is about 96 tonnes; 30% of the total train weight.

This adhesion level is ample to cope with the power and acceleration of an outer suburban train working on routes with medium station spacing. The key issue is to have

Plate 36: *Some versions of the Class 150 have end corridor connections, more suitable for routes with higher traffic levels when two or more units are coupled together. The double doors give fast access, and the original poor 2 + 3 seating layout has been much improved with better seats in a 2 + 2 configuration. The result is quite a nice local train for shorter distances on non-electrified commuter routes. This one waits at Bristol Temple Meads after arriving on a local service from Avonmouth. They are hardly ideal for long journeys though, such as the 127 miles from Gloucester to Weymouth via Bristol and Westbury, which takes 3½ hours at an average of 36 mph.*

sustained moderate acceleration up to medium speeds, limited by the available power; rather than high acceleration at low speeds, limited by adhesion. A comparable train design from the 1960s might be the highly successful Liverpool Street to Clacton / Walton 'buffet car' EMUs. These had four driven axles in a four car unit approximately the same weight as a pair of powered and unpowered triplets of the proposed train. Installed power was 1,130hp, somewhat less than the 1,500hp proposed now, and adhesive weight for traction was 34% of total train weight. Consequently, the full-length new train might have slightly lower acceleration at low speeds, but considerably greater at medium and high speeds.

Of course, with the shorter off-peak train formations the percentage of adhesive weight increases, to 39% for a three triplet formation and 56% with one or two powered triplets. In combination with the higher power to weight ratios off-peak trains will have excellent acceleration and fast journey times, simply by not discarding traction capability in off-peak periods as is done at present. The proposed solution will work very well for outer suburban routes.

A further advantage of the concept is that many of the coaches do not have traction motors and drives, giving a smoother and quieter ride. Of course, in an electric train this is far less of a problem than a diesel one, with no diesel engine under the floor to cause noise and vibration. Nevertheless, even an electric traction motor and drive does produce some noise. In one way this situation has worsened in recent years: for reasons of performance and efficiency AC traction motors are used now, driven by inverters which vary the frequency of the supply according to the speed and load. The resulting acoustic buzzes and whistles tend to carry a long distance: not so much a problem for passengers inside the coach, but an issue for those living near the tracks. No doubt many of them would prefer a return to old fashioned DC traction motors and camshaft control! Nevertheless, the smaller number of traction motors in the proposed concept should make it easier to contain such noises by careful design and appropriate acoustic shielding to produce a more environmentally-friendly solution.

The traction motors are frame-mounted with cardan shaft drives to the bogies, to keep the unsprung weight down. In fact, the drive design is identical to that used in the diesel power car for the stopping train, and components can be interchangeable with potential for reducing spares inventory costs: one standard design of 750hp powered bogie fits both kinds of train.

Both peak period and off-peak trains normally run with two powered units, so the probability of both failing in service is very low. Only the very early morning or late evening services would have a single powered triplet. Also, distances are fairly short and outer suburban routes are in relatively populated areas, so rescue is generally not far away in the rare cases of trains breaking down. Consequently, battery backup is considered unnecessary; regenerative braking in the powered triplets returns energy to the overhead line only.

If greater capacity is needed and platform lengths permit it, more unpowered and/ or powered triplets can be added to the train in any order to give the desired capacity and performance.

In common with the local stopping train, the commuter train can also use inter-city or cross country coaches without driving cabs as long as there is a driving cab at the front of the train. Since the interfaces of all vehicles are the same, there is flexibility to introduce all kinds of creative ideas to improve efficiency or services, or ease operating convenience. For example, at present a depot in a provincial city may keep some inter-city trains there until mid-morning, as they are needed for services starting then and vehicles originating elsewhere have not yet arrived. Some coaches from such trains could be borrowed for early morning commuter services, perhaps reducing the need for so many commuter coaches. If convenient the coaches could be transferred from the commuter to inter-city trains in traffic, giving through services from smaller places to distant cities. Equally, in the middle of the day when commuter coaches would otherwise lie idle in sidings, they could strengthen heavily loaded inter-city or cross country trains. Accepting the lower standards of comfort provided in the commuter coaches would be preferable to not finding a seat at all, as happens too often in current practice. All unpowered triplets can go at 150mph, whatever the seating density, whereas powered triplets are limited to 100mph.

Some degree of seat reservation capability is desirable in an outer suburban type service, particularly for off-peak traffic and any through coaches. On the other hand, the heavy peak commuter loads would probably not have reservations.

Perhaps the best compromise is to equip the powered triplets with seat reservation displays, and omit them to save costs in the unpowered triplets. The black boxes in the triplets inform the terminals whether a coach has reservation facilities or not. Seat reservation data originates from the guard's terminal in the powered triplet.

Diesel-hauled outer suburban commuter trains use the same solution as the stopping train already described: a diesel power car and a high density coach triplet with driving cab, or more of them coupled as necessary. The only difference might be the provision of first class accommodation in a few cases where demand warrants it. Most outer suburban routes would be electrified.

Inner suburban commuter trains

When distances between stations are short, say a mile or two, high speeds cannot be reached and the acceleration and braking of a train become the most important aspects of its performance. The frequent stops also demand fast access to minimise the time spent at stations; this means many (and/or wide) doors and large circulating and standing areas. This is the typical domain of the inner suburban train.

The layout of the outer suburban train described above is quite suitable for an inner suburban application when traffic levels are moderate. Seat spacing and aisle widths are satisfactory, and there are well-positioned access doors which are 1m wide. Regenerative braking is provided to give good energy efficiency. Adhesion is also adequate for a typical inner suburban service: in fact, the technical arrangements with a quarter of the axles powered are not very different from a *Class 455* inner suburban EMU.

There are some disadvantages, however. As speeds are unlikely to get above 75mph on such routes, having coach brakes suitable for 125mph and suspensions capable of 150mph is rather more expensive than necessary. Although the flexibility to improve performance with off-peak trains is valuable, a solution with fewer possibilities will be adequate for an inner suburban service. Reducing flexibility will reduce costs by having fewer couplings and simplifying control wiring.

Ideally more doors are needed to speed up access and reduce station stopping times to the minimum, with greater standing room and fewer seats to cope with exceptionally high peak loads. Toilets will not be provided on an inner suburban service, seating will be standard class only, and there will be no refreshment facilities either. Some bicycle storage space should be provided, though, separate from the seating areas to avoid tangles in crowds.

Although regenerative braking recovers much of the energy consumed due to train weight, coping with many accelerating and decelerating trains in the same area results in high currents which impose strains and costs on the electrical distribution system. Lower train weights are preferred to reduce these costs, and some weight can be saved when only lower speeds are needed. Also, an intensively worked route with short headways demands precision timing and high acceleration at low speed, so having a concept with more axles motored is preferred even though it increases costs and reduces comfort a little.

The extra width provided by the articulated concept and relatively short coach bodies is well worthwhile for an inner suburban train, and as less flexibility of length

Plate 37: *A typical inner suburban electric multiple unit has fewer facilities than the outer suburban version and a lower top speed of 75 mph. This Class 315 leaving Walthamstow Central on a London Liverpool Street to Chingford service will take 26 minutes to cover the 10½ miles with 7 stops, an average speed of 24 mph. The proposed inner suburban solution would offer greater acceleration for shorter journey times, especially in off peak periods when an unpowered coach quintuplet would be detached from the powered coach quintuplet.*

is needed some weight can be saved by having more coach bodies articulated together. A low floor with level access to platforms and many fast-opening double leaf sliding doors with wide vestibule areas free from obstructions are all necessary features for rapid loading and unloading.

These requirements result in the proposed inner suburban train design shown in *Figure 19*. Five coach bodies are articulated together in a unit 77m long, comparable in length and capacity to a conventional four car EMU but using six bogies instead of eight. As maximum speed is 75mph small wheels can be used which will fit under the low floor without requiring wheel boxes, so the layout is unrestricted.

Some further weight is saved by reducing ceiling height a little through having a flatter roof, and lighter (less comfortable!) seats are fitted. Only standard class accommodation is provided. The quintuplet still has the train information bus as usual, but only one black box is needed for the five coaches and there are no seat reservations so there is little cost penalty in adding this standard facility. Four of the six bogies are powered, those at the outer ends providing additional weight for collision protection reasons and those in the centre coach benefiting from the extra weight of the transformer and control equipment to improve adhesion. A target weight of 110 tonnes or so would be expected, giving axle loads of about 8 and 10 tonnes for the unpowered and powered bogies respectively.

At peak times, the powered inner suburban quintuplet is coupled to an unpowered quintuplet of the same length and general layout, as shown in *Figure 20*. This has a driving cab at one end only, and is very simple with its six unpowered bogies and lightweight seating. The cab end is ballasted slightly for crashworthiness reasons, but it should still be possible to manage a total weight of only about 90 tonnes for the whole quintuplet by designing it for a maximum speed of 75mph.

Consequently at peak times an inner suburban train consists of one powered and one unpowered quintuplet with a total length of 154m, weighing 200 tonnes. Adhesive weight for traction and regenerative braking is about 40% of the total train weight. Since speeds are lower, an installed power of 1,500hp will be ample, with four powered bogies and eight traction motors of 190hp each in the powered quintuplet. This gives a power to weight ratio of 7.5hp/tonne, and the good adhesion can give rapid acceleration at low speeds; just what is needed for an inner suburban duty. At off-peak times, the powered quintuplet leaves the unpowered one in a siding and runs by itself, with the power to weight ratio improving to a high 13.6hp/tonne for much improved journey speeds in spite of the many stops. In many cases it is not even necessary to have a siding to park the unpowered quintuplet; it can just be left behind in the platform at a terminus and remain there until needed later in the day for the evening peak service.

Of course, regenerative braking is provided, being able to reduce energy costs significantly by recovering power from the frequent stops. Since the power consumption of the inner suburban quintuplet is the same as the outer suburban triplet, the same transformer can be used; its provision of hotel power is also the same. In addition, the control gear of inner and outer suburban trains is not very different so there is scope for achieving economies of scale with standard equipment to a common design. No battery backup is needed in either case.

Compared to a conventional four-car EMU solution the proposed inner suburban train should be economical, with a peak period train having only twenty-four axles instead of thirty-two, three driving cabs instead of four and one transformer and pantograph instead of two. Its off-peak average speed will also be far superior.

Any number of quintuplets, powered or unpowered, can be coupled together as needed, subject to platform lengths and the level of performance desired. The control signals are just the same as the other trains described, and cabs are switched in and out when trains are combined and divided in exactly the same way. On a route with high traffic densities, one powered quintuplet could be coupled to two unpowered quintuplets at peak times. This would result in a high capacity train 231m long with a reasonable power to weight ratio of 5.2hp/tonne, still better than a *Class 315* for example.

Other vehicles designed for the other kinds of trains described can be coupled to the quintuplets too, either to haul or be hauled by them. The standardised train information bus informs the driver which vehicles are in the formation and what can and cannot be done. Of course, if an inner suburban quintuplet is in the formation, speed is limited to 75mph, but if that constraint is acceptable an inner suburban quintuplet can haul (for example) an inter-city coach triplet or a sleeping car triplet. Although this flexibility might not be needed much for regular services, it could be very useful at times of disruption or for moving empty stock around the network.

For medium-distance commuter trains the choice of solution depends on the local circumstances. If a city has only a few such routes but more long-distance services, it may be more convenient to have the greater flexibility of the outer suburban train designs described earlier and not bother with the inner suburban design at all. On the other hand, if a short-distance urban service is the main focus with very high traffic levels and congested city centre routes, the inner suburban solution may be preferred. The inner suburban solution is also suitable for short-distance inter-urban or semi-rural routes with frequent stops where high speeds are not possible and minimal train facilities are adequate.

No special solution is proposed for diesel operated inner suburban trains: the stopping train design is used in this case. There are few such services now, and they would justify electrification in the medium-term anyway.

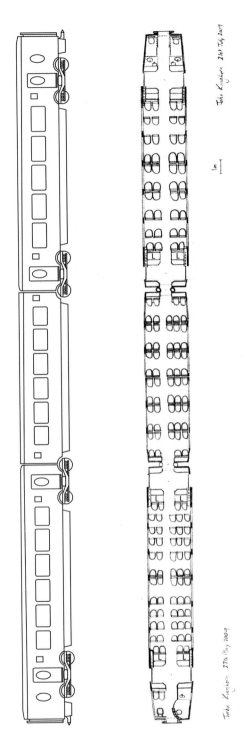

Figure 16: *Long distance commuter composite coach triplet*
   L luggage rack

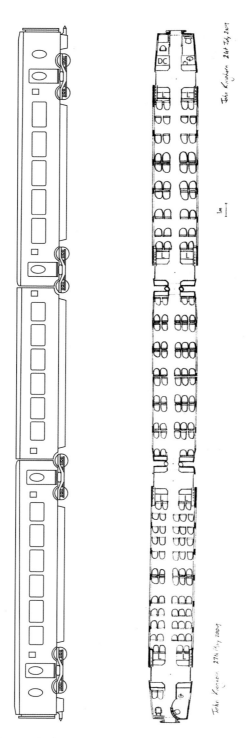

Figure 17: *Unpowered outer suburban composite coach triplet*
L luggage rack DC driving cab

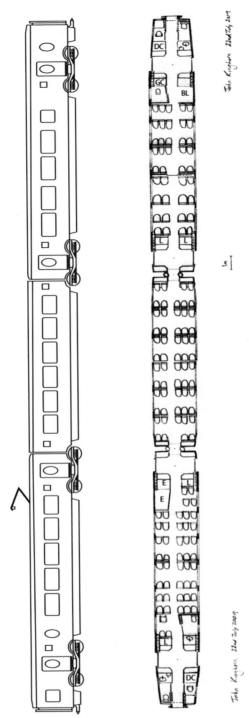

Figure 18: *Powered outer suburban coach triplet*
L luggage rack E electrical equipment
GC guards' compartment BL bicycles and luggage storage   DC driving cab

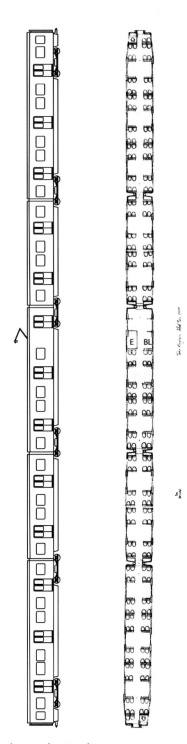

Figure 19: *Powered inner suburban coach quintuplet*
E electrical equipment BL bicycles and luggage storage

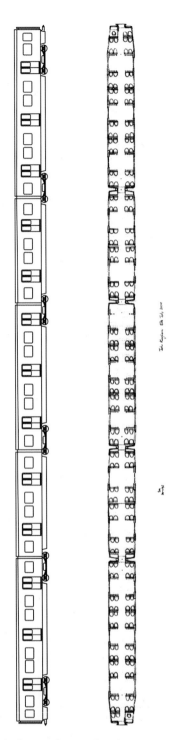

Figure 20: *Unpowered inner suburban coach quintuplet*

Chapter 15

Third rail electric trains

So far the electric trains described have been designed for the 25kV 50Hz AC overhead electrification system, but there are DC electrification systems too. Discounting underground, metro and tramway systems, which are outside the scope of this book, there is a substantial route mileage of the British rail network electrified using the third rail system at 750V DC.

A commuter network round Liverpool uses this system, which is largely self-contained. When the time comes to renew its trains, DC versions of the inner or outer suburban train designs described above could be used. There is no strong need for compatibility with other trains though: they will remain in the local area. If it is decided to electrify the lines from Southport to Preston, Manchester and Ormskirk, the short section between Burscough and Southport could be dual electrified with AC overhead and DC third rail for flexibility to accept either kind of electric train.

Southern England is a more complex story. Already most routes south of the Thames to all the south coast towns as far west as Weymouth are electrified on the third rail system. It is proposed that the remaining routes in this area would also be electrified by 2035 using the same system. In many cases, the northern boundary of these services is a London terminus, so to a large extent the system is self-contained. There are some through services, however, which involve changing electrification systems.

The principal boundaries between electrification systems for London-oriented services currently are on the Thameslink and West London routes. Shortly the new Javelin services from Kent will join them, changing from DC to AC for the section on the High Speed 1 line to St Pancras. A new southwards link from Heathrow airport will require another boundary between electrification systems.

Reading will also be a boundary, with AC on the Great Western main line and DC on the routes via Wokingham. It is proposed that the line from Basingstoke to Reading would be electrified on the DC system, to facilitate services such as Portsmouth to Reading with DC-only trains. Salisbury is another obvious boundary point: eastwards

Plate 38: *One of the earliest British suburban electrification schemes was the line from Liverpool to Southport, inaugurated in 1904. This pioneering route forms part of a third rail DC local electric network for Merseyside which now extends to Chester. At Southport an electric train from Hunts Cross via Liverpool Central has just arrived on the left, a journey of 26 miles covered in an hour with 20 stops. On the right, a Pacer prepares to bounce the 45 miles to Rochdale via Wigan and Manchester in 1¾ hours, an average of 27 mph.*

to Basingstoke, Eastleigh and Southampton would be DC, westwards to Exeter and northwards to Westbury would be AC. Probably the Bristol to Weymouth route would remain diesel-operated even in 2035; in the longer term Dorchester would be the point where AC met DC.

Currently the entire third rail area has multiple unit electric trains with maximum speeds of 100mph and a predominantly commuter-like character. Apart from small improvements such as the addition of air-conditioning on many trains, a reincarnated Sir Herbert Walker would recognise the services as following exactly the same strategy as he pursued for the Southern Railway in the 1930s. It is essentially a steam age infrastructure electrified, with no route improvements since that era.

The dominance of London commuting in the area, together with its geography, has tended to reinforce the idea that this level of performance is adequate. Relatively short distances of fifty to eighty miles from London to the south coast, high population densities and a largely captive commuter market imply that average speeds of 50-60mph will do.

Plate 39: *The routes from London to Brighton, Portsmouth, Eastbourne and Hastings were all electrified in the mid-1930s, Britain's first 'main line' electrification schemes. They were highly successful, and a similar pattern of operating continues today. Although slow by modern standards, good services are provided to local stations and they are well used. A three coach electric multiple unit arrives at Falmer on a Brighton to Seaford service, a journey of 17 miles which takes 36 minutes at an average of 28 mph.*

There are, however, some long-distance non-London flows as well. The third rail area is about 170 miles long from east to west, and there are through services to points westwards and northwards too. At present a passenger going from Hastings to Bournemouth on the 'direct' south coast lines (130 rail miles) will find that the journey takes nearly four hours with two changes, an average speed of 34mph. This is the same distance as Stevenage to Doncaster on the East Coast main line, taking one-and-a-half hours. Cross country trains capable of running at 125mph are compelled to dawdle at 100mph when they venture into this area. Consequently there is plenty of scope for improvement, and many more non-commuter passengers could be attracted to faster services.

In fact, some lines in the south are well aligned for fast speeds, Ashford to Redhill and Woking to Southampton being prime examples. Some infrastructure improvements are proposed to make better use of the network assets.

At Redhill, halfway between London and Brighton, there would be a flyover from east to west, and also a west to south spur. With electrification of the missing sections

Plate 40: *Further electrifications on the third rail system of southern England were undertaken in the 1960s and 1980s, and that network now includes some quite long distance services. This train from Weymouth to London Waterloo, seen departing from Southampton, will travel 143 miles in 2¾ hours, an average speed of 52 mph. At present all trains operating on the third rail system are limited to a maximum of 100 mph, but routes such as this are well aligned and it is possible to go faster as proposed in the strategy.*

towards Reading, and upgrading in general, this would create a prime inter-city route through the centre of the region. Rather than being just a local connecting service, fast long-distance trains would run from Ashford and Brighton via Guildford to Reading, Oxford, Birmingham and beyond. A short spur from Shalford to the Portsmouth main line south of Guildford would allow fast services from Ashford to Havant, Portsmouth, Southampton and points west. Many journeys across this heavily populated region would be improved dramatically, avoiding much travel via London and helping to reduce congestion in that area. There are significant benefits for freight too.

On the south coast route, four infrastructure improvements are suggested. There would be a south to east spur at Eastleigh, and the line from there to Fareham would be doubled throughout, including widening Fareham tunnel. This would then become the main route eastwards from Southampton for services such as Cardiff to Portsmouth and Poole to Brighton, with the important regional airport at Southampton becoming more accessible by direct train services from all parts of its catchment area. The existing route via Swanwick would then be freed up for a more frequent service of local trains. Secondly, a bypass line in the Ford area would eliminate the speed restrictions of the

Plate 41: *Previous generations of outer suburban trains on the southern third rail network were all replaced quite recently with new 100 mph air-conditioned trains. Although power supplies have been upgraded to cope with the higher current demands of these trains, schedules often remain more or less the same as those of 40 or more years ago. This four car electric multiple unit passes through the New Forest on a Poole to London Waterloo stopping service, a 114 mile journey taking nearly 3 hours with 20 stops at an average of 41 mph. It will be overtaken en route by a faster service.*

current route, allowing the section between Worthing and Havant to exploit its straight alignment for high speeds. Efforts should be directed to removing level crossings in the area too. Thirdly, the direct line between Polegate and Pevensey would be reinstated, allowing some fast services to bypass Eastbourne. Finally, the route from Ashford to Hastings would be electrified and redoubled throughout.

These improvements create two prime east to west inter-city routes in the region, converging on the important hub of Ashford International, which is seriously under-utilised for international trains at present. Fast direct services to it from all parts of southern England, bypassing awkward connections in London, would help to realise the full potential of that hub as a gateway from the region to Europe.

Since the longer distance services in the third rail area have been re-equipped with new trains recently, there is little scope now to transform London-oriented commuter services from most places for a generation. Kent will get an improvement with the introduction of Javelin services to St Pancras, but Sussex will see little change except some modest speeding up to places like Chichester. For the eastern parts of Hampshire

Plate 42: *Inner suburban trains need wide double doors for fast access, as minimizing time spent at stations is critical to achieve reasonable average speeds in the 25 mph range when there are frequent stops. These inner suburban trains at Clapham Junction have such doors, but there is still the obstacle of a step to cause delay. The proposed strategy provides level access from the platform without a step, reducing delay especially when passengers are loading heavy luggage.*

there will be few changes either, but the main line from Waterloo to Bournemouth should be upgraded for high speeds where the curvature permits. The upgrading of the main line from London to Basingstoke also enables the introduction of fast services from Waterloo to Exeter, electrified throughout with a change between DC and AC systems at Salisbury.

This summary of route characteristics gives the background for new third rail trains in the region: most of them need to operate on both AC and DC systems. Given the flexibility of the proposed rolling stock strategy, it would be perfectly possible to switch locomotives or power cars, just as is done elsewhere between electric and diesel traction. Dual voltage solutions are better, however, and this approach is proposed.

Long-distance inter-city type trains with medium- to high-capacity are needed for Waterloo to Weymouth, Waterloo to Exeter, Birmingham to Ashford or Brighton via Reading and Guildford, Birmingham to Bournemouth, Cardiff to Portsmouth, Southampton to Ashford via Reigate and Poole to Ashford via Brighton services. Essentially the same solution is proposed as inter-city trains elsewhere. A dual voltage version of the inter-city electric locomotive is needed, with the same coaches and driving

MarketPlace	: Ebay
Order Number	: 141624589410-1124313880004
Ship Method	: Other Courier 3-5 days
Order Date	: 2015-05-07
Email	: davelewis5665@hotmail.co.uk

Items : 1

Qty	Item	Locator
1	Beyond the HST	HOL-3-LM-044-03-25
	ISBN : 190704065X	RY

RCode:

We hope that you are completely satisfied with your purchase and ask you to leave positive feedback accordingly.

However, if you are unsatisfied with your order, please contact us by telephone or email. We will do whatever it takes to resolve the issue.

Mulberry House, Woods Way, Goring By Sea, West Sussex, BN12 4QY. Tel:+44(0)1903 507544
Email: ebay@worldofbooks.com | Twitter: @WorldofBooksltd | Web: www.worldofbooks.com

Plate 43: *A typical inner suburban train concept uses four car multiple units, coupled in pairs at peak times, as seen in this example at Clapham Junction. Some routes have very heavy peak loads, and longer trains would be better. The proposed strategy uses articulated coach quintuplets in powered and unpowered versions, allowing the unpowered ones to be uncoupled at off peak times and thus improve acceleration then for faster schedules.*

trailer as described earlier. The third rail electrical system does, however, impose some serious technical constraints, which need to be solved.

The first question is how to deal with intermittent current collection. Inevitably, junctions need gaps in the third rail, and ice, lubricant, sand, leaves and other debris may interfere with the conductivity of the interface between the third rail and the current collection shoe. Traditionally this is dealt with by having several current collection shoes spaced through the train, connected together so that with a bit of luck at least one of them is working reasonably well at any instant. The approach also keeps average currents from each shoe down to reasonable levels, and reduces EMC (Electro Magnetic Compatibility) problems. This approach has the disadvantage of requiring considerable lengths of rather heavy wiring, plus tricky connections between vehicles especially when they can be separated. The traditional thick cable for the connections between vehicles has been replaced by many thinner cables in most modern DC trains, but clearly there are significant costs involved whichever option is chosen: copper is expensive stuff. Also flexibility is reduced to some extent, as vehicles for third rail areas then become 'special' as they contain facilities not needed elsewhere.

Plate 44: *The North London line and the local Euston to Watford services comprise the remaining third rail DC 'main line' operations outside the Merseyside and former Southern Region areas. Recently transferred to Transport for London responsibility, they will be linked to south London via an extended East London line to form key orbital routes in the capital. With close station spacing and moderately frequent services their inner suburban character approaches an urban metro operation. This new Class 378 multiple unit pauses at Caledonian Road and Barnsbury station on a Richmond to Stratford service. The 17 mile journey with 21 intermediate stops takes about an hour.*

An alternative approach is to have multiple current collection shoes on the locomotive or power car only, and to provide energy storage to smooth out the inevitable disruptions in the current flow. This can be done mechanically; in the 1940s a third rail electric locomotive was developed using a 'booster' control concept with a motor-generator driving a one tonne flywheel which increased speed when power was available and reduced speed when it supplied power.

A more modern energy storage option is electrical: either lithium ion batteries or perhaps supercapacitors would be suitable. Some massive current transients are involved when the train is accelerating under full power and current collection fails: on the other hand, the storage capacity required is not high as the period of intermittency is short. Whether the energy storage and control technologies described are yet robust enough to stand up to such arduous conditions is not clear to the author, nor is the relative cost effectiveness of the alternatives. However, there is no doubt that transient current smoothing can be done and consequently power collection shoes on

Plate 45: *There is a small third rail system in the Isle of Wight, electrified in the 1960s. At present it is operated by shortened ex-London Underground tube trains dating from 1938, clearances being insufficient for standard British rolling stock. A Ryde Pier Head to Shanklin service is seen near Brading, the 8.5 mile journey taking 24 minutes with 6 stops at an average speed of 21 mph. The proposed inner suburban train has low height coaches, and might be a suitable replacement for the present rolling stock if and when new trains can be afforded.*

the locomotive only will be enough. Whichever energy storage method is chosen, the approach avoids the complications and cost of high current traction power wiring in the coaches, and they can be just the same as those used anywhere else.

A second issue to consider is current collection at high speeds. Third rail operation at 100mph has been well established for many years; however the system has been traditionally more common for lower speed urban networks. The performance of third rail current collection at 150mph probably needs more research. From a mechanical point of view, it should be satisfactory if care is taken to have gradual slopes at the ends of the conductor rails leading to gaps; this will limit the transient forces on current collection shoes as they move off and on the rails. At present the shoe dynamics seem to be relatively simple, relying on weight primarily for contact. If necessary for higher speeds, a more complex dynamic system involving springs and dampers could be considered, but the operating conditions are not dramatically different from established practice. Maybe some new materials would be of benefit, or the use of more lightweight shoes rather than fewer heavy ones. Anyway, it is assumed that such issues will not prove insuperable and adequate third rail current collection is achievable at speeds up to 150mph.

The third issue is the question of current levels. The electric locomotive has an installed power of 6,000hp, 88% more than the 3,200hp 4REP units of the 1960s Bournemouth electrification. This is not surprising; air resistance is the dominant factor in energy consumption in this case and it increases as the square of the speed; 2.25 times greater at 150mph compared with 100mph. Relative to more modern EMU trains the power levels of the proposed locomotive are still rather high; 48% more than the 4,050hp of a twelve-car *Class 450* formation, for example. Clearly the third rail power supply will need to be strengthened for high speed stretches using the proposed inter-city trains.

On the other hand, the fast inter-city services proposed in the third rail area will be less frequent than the intensive London-oriented commuter services, so usually it will be a case of a few high current trains rather than many lower current ones. The busiest section, between Redhill and Shalford, might have six inter-city trains per hour (two from Brighton and four from Ashford), but line curvature of this section may restrict speeds to 125mph at best so current demands per train will not be so high. Also, there will not be such a pronounced peak in traffic in rush hour periods compared to a commuter route; the same frequency of trains will probably operate all day. So, in terms of peak current demands, the third rail system for these fast inter-city services is probably little different from an intensively-worked outer suburban commuter route.

With the relatively low voltages and high currents, power losses in the DC system are high unless the substations are fairly close together. The geography of the area helps this situation for the new inter-city services, though, as their east–west routes are frequently crossed by or merged with north–south commuter routes. Consequently there are plenty of substations around to share the load, ready to be adapted and upgraded without the need for many new locations. For example, at Dorking a substation exists on the long-electrified north–south route, a short distance from the presently unelectrified east–west route.

In spite of all these factors, it is possible that electrical losses in getting power to the inter-city trains in third rail areas might be considered too high, especially through the locomotive's own shoegear. If so, a simple solution would be to have conductor rails on both sides of the track in high speed areas: current through each rail and set of shoes is halved, voltage drop is also halved and electrical losses due to those components are cut to a quarter of previous levels on each side, halving losses overall. The cost of the track increases, of course, so it is a balance to decide whether the reduced electrical losses are enough to compensate for the extra capital cost. Such measures are only necessary where high currents are being drawn, however; for lower speeds or downhill gradients the standard single conductor rail will be sufficient. The inter-city train is able to travel anywhere on the third rail network, of course, but power supply limitations may restrict it to 100mph and lower acceleration where the system has not been upgraded to cope with its higher current demands.

Since the coaches in the proposed strategy rely on 50Hz AC single phase hotel power, this needs to be provided by the locomotive as a conversion from the 750V DC supply in third rail areas. If the mechanical energy storage system is used, hotel power can be provided fairly easily by windings on the motor generator and a suitable control system. On the other hand if battery or supercapacitor technology is preferred for energy storage, an inverter is needed to convert DC to AC for hotel power. Either of these arrangements can be made in the locomotive without needing too much extra weight or space, so the AC/DC locomotive is nearly the same as the AC only version, the only visible difference being the addition of power collection shoes. Of course, the locomotive power system needs to be adapted for AC or DC supplies too: not very difficult if the requirement for the option has been designed in from the start.

The above facilities will make the dual voltage locomotive a bit more expensive than the standard AC-only version, but since a reasonable number are needed, development costs per unit should not be too high. Of course, these locomotives can be freely used in AC areas only if required. Probably the extra costs for the DC facility will result in most locomotives being AC only, however, rather than choosing the greater flexibility of making all locomotives AC/DC.

So, that covers the inter-city and long-distance commuter trains passing through third rail areas; what about other types of train?

An outer suburban DC only train can easily be made using the same powered triplet as the 100mph AC train, adapted to the third rail supply. This has the same flexibility to improve off-peak services as described in Chapter 14 above, and is a recommended solution in the long-term. Since, however, the entire third rail outer suburban fleet has been renewed in recent years, train operating companies will be reluctant to invest in a new train design which is incompatible with their current rolling stock. This is especially true where the train manufacturer provides maintenance facilities: for practical purposes the local operating area for a set of routes is locked into one manufacturer's products as they run the depots. Consequently, any need for additional capacity will probably be met by ordering more trains of the existing design.

As there has been a large re-equipment at the same time, there is little hope of improving the situation significantly in the third rail outer suburban area until 2040 or so unless the new trains are wastefully retired early. The best strategy in the meantime may be to upgrade a few longer distance lines to inter-city status as described above, cascading their existing trains to other routes to handle demands for increased capacity.

Consequently, there will be no need for a DC-only version of the proposed outer suburban train for many years yet.

A more useful train would be an AC/DC version of the outer suburban powered triplet. This can cover services crossing the boundaries between electrification systems, and of course has the flexibility to operate in either area alone if necessary. Apart from a small extra cost to add an inverter providing AC hotel power for the coaches, adding pickup shoes and modifying the motor control system to accept AC or DC inputs, the train is identical to the standard AC-only version. Such a train would find application on the west London line, services from north to south through the new Heathrow route (Airtrack), local services through Salisbury, etc. It might also be useful in the Liverpool / Southport / Chester areas.

Since the power collection shoes at both ends of the AC/DC outer suburban powered triplet are far enough apart, there should be no need for transient power storage or through traction bus wiring to other vehicles. The unpowered outer suburban triplet design appropriate here is thus identical to the standard version used for AC trains.

The solution would also be suitable for the *Thameslink* upgrade, but it is a bit too late for trains to be designed in time and the intensive service with short headways through the central section will demand automatic train operation. That will not be a standard network-wide requirement for many years. Probably a fixed formation and power to weight ratio will be desired there too; consequently the flexibility of the proposed solution would be difficult to exploit there and there are fewer advantages then compared with a conventional EMU approach. The low floor would be an advantage, but it might be questioned whether there are enough doors for such high peak loads. Probably a dedicated AC/DC solution intermediate between the outer and inner suburban concepts described here would fit best in these special circumstances.

A DC-only version of the inner suburban train described above would be suitable for south London when new trains are needed there. There is no obvious need for an AC/DC version in the medium term.

Chapter 16

Through coaches and changing formations

Many years ago, the long-distance train conveying through coaches to multiple destinations on different routes was a common feature of railway operations. It was possible to board the Atlantic Coast Express at London Waterloo and end up in Seaton, Sidmouth, Exmouth, Ilfracombe, Torrington, Plymouth, Padstow or Bude by joining the appropriate coach. Although this degree of splitting a train into sections was exceptional, many smaller places throughout the country enjoyed some through services to distant big cities using this approach even when traffic levels were quite low.

The technique hardly exists now. For reasons of operating convenience, incompatibilities of rolling stock and the effects of organisational structures, long-distance passengers to most smaller places need to change trains at present. This is OK when connections are good, trains are running on time and station layouts are convenient. Sometimes, however, there are long waits for connections giving unattractive through journey times, or conversely tight timings prompting 'Will-I-make-it?' thoughts in the mind of the passenger. Other hazards for the infrequent traveller may include unfamiliar station layouts, bridges and subways to navigate with luggage or infants, uncertainties about platform numbers and connecting train departure times, whether there will be enough seats in the next train, etc.

It is easy for seasoned rail travellers to dismiss such perceived limitations as trivial, but undoubtedly they are significant factors inhibiting some people from considering rail travel as an option. From the passenger's point of view, a through carriage to the final destination is an attractive proposition. Even if the process of changing train formations takes a few minutes, this is still likely to be quicker than the time necessary for transfer to a connecting train with a high chance of catching it. No shifting of luggage is needed, and if the train is running a little late it does not matter so much; the seat the passenger is occupying will still get to the destination desired.

There are also some operational advantages in splitting trains as well as inconveniences. On a congested main line, it is a waste of line capacity to have many separate short trains serving less popular destinations. If instead these are combined into fewer long trains on the congested route, and then split to go their various ways in less busy locations, this frees up capacity for other services. It also requires fewer resources using the proposed locomotive-hauled strategy; only one locomotive is needed for part of the journey, and fewer drivers are needed to run the service overall. In many cases it can also avoid diesel haulage in electrified areas, giving improvements in energy efficiency and less pollution.

Splitting trains is also useful where loadings vary markedly on a route; coaches can be left behind at popular locations and re-used for other services, while the shorter train continues to the less popular destinations. Quite often these places may be at the boundaries of electrified areas too, so a change of traction and a change of train length can be carried out at the same time.

Since all the proposed vehicles can be coupled to each other and the traction, braking and communication interfaces are all standardised, there is great flexibility to change train formations in many ways to suit individual requirements. Some examples are described here to give an indication of the possibilities.

First, consider the combination and splitting of long-distance electric inter-city trains where the top speed of 150mph is needed throughout the routes. This would be done to minimise locomotive resources and line occupation on a heavily used trunk route, while providing through services with lesser flows at one or both ends of the journey. The high speed demands a streamlined locomotive and driving trailer at either end of the train on all parts of the route.

An example might be a **Newcastle and Leeds to Paignton and Plymouth** service, as shown in *Figure 21*. Trains of three triplets each are electrically propelled from Newcastle and Leeds to Sheffield. There the electric locomotive of the front train and the driving trailer of the rear train are removed. The combined six-triplet train is electrically propelled via Birmingham and Bristol to Exeter, where the train splits into a front four-triplet section and a rear two-triplet section. An electric locomotive is added to the rear of the front section, which departs for Plymouth. A driving trailer is added to the front of the rear section, which proceeds to Torquay and Paignton.

A second category of train formation alterations occurs when there is a change of motive power for one or more of the sections of an inter-city train. This will be of most interest for combining trains for multiple destinations to save line capacity on a trunk route.

An example might be a **London to Glasgow and Aberdeen via Edinburgh** service, as shown in *Figure 22*. This assumes a situation in a few years where the direct Edinburgh to Glasgow route has been electrified but not yet the route from Edinburgh to Aberdeen. An off-peak train of five triplets is electrically-hauled from King's Cross to Edinburgh, where it splits into a front three-triplet section and a rear two-triplet section. A driving trailer is attached to the rear of the front section, which can depart for Glasgow on the direct route: the train is now short enough to fit into Queen Street station. A diesel locomotive is attached to the front of the rear section, which departs for Aberdeen, the two triplets being within the capability of a single ex-HST diesel power car for reasonable average speeds. At busier times, a *Class 67* or two ex-HST power cars would be used instead on a longer train.

Changing formations by adding or removing both locomotives and driving trailers is rather time-consuming and demands mid-platform crossover facilities or more extensive shunting. Another option is to couple complete trains together for efficiency on a congested main line, making it easy to split them at a junction. Traction types can be mixed as well if necessary.

An example might be a **London to Hull and Leeds** service, as shown in *Figure 23*. Currently the route between Doncaster and Hull is not electrified, but it is desirable for efficiency and pollution reasons to avoid diesel traction on the main line between London and Doncaster. So the train consists of a front Leeds portion with electric locomotive, three coach triplets and a driving trailer, coupled to a rear Hull portion with an ex-HST diesel power car, two coach triplets and a driving trailer. The diesel engine is shut down between London and Doncaster, with the electric locomotive providing traction for the complete 330m-long train. Both driving trailers and the locomotive contribute to regenerative braking for the train's 630 tonnes, and a reasonable power to weight ratio of 9.5hp/tonne is available. The sections split at Doncaster, and the diesel engine is powered up on the rear section for the trip to Hull while the electric section continues to Leeds.

There are some minor snags with this approach. Firstly, access between the two train sections is not possible because of the streamlined ends. This is no worse than the current method of coupling two Voyager sets together on similar trains. Secondly, the diesel ex-HST power car is limited to 125mph, so unless it is upgraded for 150mph when being hauled the combined train cannot go quite so fast. This might be acceptable for a 'semi-fast' type of service with more intermediate stopping points. Thirdly, the gap between the two sections of train will cause greater aerodynamic drag and consequently lower energy efficiency. At the lower speed of 125mph this should not be too serious, however.

An alternative option is to leave out the ex-HST diesel power car from the London to Doncaster formation. This reduces weight and avoids dragging an unused vehicle on the electrified network, and also permits the full 150mph speed in theory. On the other hand, the 'blunt' front end of the rear section is not a happy match with the streamlined rear end of the front section, and the resulting vortices will give extra aerodynamic drag and lower energy efficiency somewhat. Also adding the power car at Doncaster increases shunting delays a little, although the Leeds portion can get away quickly. It is a kind of intermediate solution between the first two alternatives, which might be useful if the resulting balance of compromises is acceptable. Aesthetically it will be unattractive!

In cases where high speed is only needed on the main trunk route and 100mph maximum speeds will do for sections of trains at the extremities, another approach is possible for inter-city or cross country routes. This uses coaches with cabs at the splitting point, and is especially useful where trains are being shortened to match lower demand.

An example might be a **Waterloo to Bournemouth and Weymouth** service, as shown in *Figure 24*. Trains of five triplets are electrically-hauled by an AC/DC locomotive to Bournemouth, with the second and third triplets having adjacent driving cabs. Maximum speed is 150mph. At Bournemouth the train splits into a front section of two triplets, which proceeds to Weymouth. Although now restricted to 125mph as there is no longer regenerative braking help from a driving trailer, the front section's weight is now 235 tonnes and the potential power to weight ratio increases to a stunning 25hp/ tonne. This would allow very fast acceleration from the more frequent stops.

In practice, however, the power supply for that section would not be upgraded to allow such high performance, but a good average speed should still be possible. The rear section of the train, detached at Bournemouth, is propelled into a siding using battery power from the driving trailer, driven from the leading coach cab. It is later hauled by the driving trailer to the up platform to await the arrival of the next service from Weymouth, which attaches to the rear. The combined five-triplet train is then electrically propelled back to Waterloo, the maximum speed being 150mph again.

There are some minor snags with the approach. On the up journey from Weymouth to Bournemouth, speed will be limited to 100mph rather than 125mph because of the 'blunt' leading cab end; just the same as at present. There is no emergency power backup for trains on the Weymouth to Bournemouth section; but failure of the third rail supply is a rare event, and the situation is no worse than the present anyway. Limited bicycle storage facilities would be provided in the coach with a cab used for the Weymouth portions, and if catering is required on the outer section it would be provided using a catering trolley.

A minor variant of the above example might occur at Salisbury, where in addition to detaching a rear section from Waterloo the locomotive also switches from DC to AC operation before heading for Yeovil or Exeter. In this case, without the power supply restriction, the train can accelerate away from intermediate stations very quickly.

Quite often a change of traction type will occur when traffic density changes, so it is convenient to change the length of train and locomotive at the same time. The formation of the train can be arranged to take advantage of the geography of the specific situation.

An example might be a **London to Swansea and Pembroke Dock** service, as shown in *Figure 25*. This assumes that London Paddington to Swansea is electrified, and the route beyond in west Wales is not. Since the route involves a reversal at the Swansea terminus, it is most convenient to have the locomotive at the east end of the train. A train of four coach triplets is propelled from Paddington to Swansea, with the second triplet having a westward facing cab. Top speed is 150mph. At Swansea, the train splits and the electric locomotive and the rear three triplets shunt into a siding, leaving the driving trailer and one triplet in the platform. An ex-HST diesel power car then shunts on to the rear of the train in the platform, which now becomes the front of course. The train of diesel locomotive, one triplet and driving trailer then proceeds to Pembroke Dock, the capacity being sufficient for that section and the train having a good power to weight ratio of 11hp/tonne to give fast acceleration from the intermediate stops. Top speed now is 125mph.

On the return journey, the train from Pembroke Dock arrives at the terminal platform in Swansea first, then the diesel power car is detached and proceeds to a siding. Three coach triplets, driven from the leading cab in the first coach, are then propelled by an electric locomotive from another siding to join the rear of the train in the platform. The complete train of four triplets, with the electric locomotive leading, then departs for London, maximum speed 150mph again.

Where speeds do not exceed 125mph anywhere it is possible to have locomotives at both ends of the train and dispense with the driving trailer. With diesel locomotives there will be no regenerative braking at all, so energy efficiency will be poorer and brake wear higher (although no worse than at present). There will be no emergency power backup either. Effectively it is a new HST with the same power cars and new coaches. This kind of formation can become more flexible, however, through the use of coaches with cabs that allow the train to be split. It might be useful where multiple destinations are served from a hilly core route needing higher power and where lower speeds for the split sections will do.

An example might be an **Inverness to Glasgow and Edinburgh** service, as shown in *Figure 26*. The train has ex-HST diesel power cars at either end, with four coach triplets between them. Triplets two and three have facing driving cabs in the middle of the train. The whole train proceeds from Inverness to Perth with a power to weight ratio of 10.5hp/tonne, sufficient for the steep hills, and could go at 125mph if it got the chance. At Perth the train splits in the middle, the front section proceeding to Glasgow. It can still go at 125mph as it has a (sort of!) streamlined front end. The rear section heads for Edinburgh, where its 100mph top speed due to the leading coach cab is not a limitation on the tortuous route through Fife.

On the return journey, the Glasgow to Perth section is now limited to 100mph as the coach cab is leading, which is a pity but no worse than at present. It couples to the rear of the Edinburgh section which gets to Perth first, and the combined train returns to Inverness.

As mentioned earlier, there might be occasions where inter-city or cross country coaches are borrowed to help out on commuter trains at peak periods. This means transferring them back again at off-peak commuting times, presenting the opportunity to offer long-distance through coaches to and from smaller places. The coaches can be transferred freely, regardless of whether the local or main line services are electric or diesel.

An example in an 'all electric' environment might be a **Skipton to Leeds and London** service, as shown in *Figure 27*. A local Skipton to Leeds stopping service at peak periods consists of a powered outer suburban triplet propelling an unpowered inter-city triplet with a driving cab. At Leeds, a mid-morning London-bound inter-city service waits in the platform with its locomotive at the east end, having four triplets but, for the moment, without its driving trailer, which lurks in a nearby siding. The local train arrives at Leeds and attaches to the end of the inter-city train. Then, the local train splits and the powered outer suburban triplet returns to Skipton as an off-peak stopping train. Once the local train has cleared the platform the driving trailer emerges from the siding and joins on to the end of the inter-city train, using its own battery power. The combined inter-city train, including the through coaches from Skipton, is then propelled to London.

In the evening, the whole process is reversed with the local train borrowing an inter-city coach triplet, complete with through passengers, to give extra capacity in the peak period.

An 'all diesel' example of combining local and cross country services to provide through coaches might be a **Lowestoft to Norwich and Birmingham** service as shown in *Figure 28*. A local stopping train from Lowestoft to Norwich in the peak commuting period consists of an inter-city type coach triplet with cab propelled by a diesel power car. Maximum speed is 100mph. At Norwich a cross country train comprising an ex-HST diesel power car and a standard inter-city coach triplet waits in the platform. Nearby, a driving trailer waits in a siding. When the local train arrives at Norwich it couples on to the cross country train. The diesel power car then splits from the coaches, and returns as a local stopping train to Lowestoft by itself. Next the driving trailer emerges from the siding under battery power and couples onto the cross country train. The cross country train, now consisting of driving trailer, two coach triplets and ex-HST diesel power car, then departs for Birmingham. It has a maximum speed of 125mph and an adequate power to weight ratio of 8.1hp/tonne, suitable for the fairly flat route.

Diesel and electric power units can be combined together, to avoid the need for shunting at the boundaries of electrification. An example might be a **Matlock to Derby, Nottingham and Lincoln** service, as shown in *Figure 29*. A local diesel power car is coupled to an electric powered outer suburban triplet, giving a total train weight of 130 tonnes and seating capacity of 136. It is assumed that the section between Ambergate (junction for the Matlock branch) through Derby to Nottingham is electrified, and the Matlock branch itself and Nottingham to Lincoln are not. No shunting is needed, and the diesel engine can be shut down for the central electrified section. The nominal power to weight ratio is 5.8hp/tonne on diesel power, fairly low but adequate for the extremities of the route and battery boost is available from energy stored by regenerative braking. On electric power, the performance improves to a rather good 11.5hp/tonne, with again some battery boost available to improve further. Maximum speed throughout is 100mph.

As mentioned earlier, trains powered by diesel power cars or electric outer suburban triplets can be combined together and split as easily as conventional DMUs and EMUs. Unpowered trailers can be added or removed freely to give optimum matches between desired capacity and performance, or simply for operational convenience. All the shunting techniques described above can be used as well, with ample scope for imaginative operators to think up creative solutions appropriate to their particular needs.

Recreating the grand multi-portioned trains of the past is perfectly possible if required. As a modern successor to the Atlantic Coast Express, consider for example a **London Waterloo to Exeter / Exmouth / Barnstaple / Paignton / Plymouth / Tavistock / Newquay / Penzance** service as shown in *Figure 30*. This assumes electrification from Waterloo to Exeter and on to Plymouth, together with the Paignton branch, and reinstatement of the line to Tavistock.

A long six-triplet train, hauled by an AC/DC electric locomotive, covers the journey from Waterloo to Exeter Central, maximum speed 150mph. All triplets except the first have driving cabs. The locomotive changes from DC to AC supply at the Salisbury stop.

On arrival at Exeter Central, the train splits after the fourth triplet, and using battery power the driving trailer moves the rear two triplets to another platform. A diesel power car arrives from the west as an off-peak stopping service from Barnstaple, and couples to the two triplets. The driving trailer then detaches itself from the coaches and rejoins the main train, which departs for Exeter St Davids.

Next, a diesel power car arrives on an off-peak service from Exmouth and couples up to the east end of the coaches remaining at Exeter Central. Now the formation is split in the middle, forming two trains; each consists of a diesel power car hauling a coach triplet. The western one heads back to Barnstaple, and the eastern one departs for Exmouth. Maximum speed for both of these sections is 100mph.

In the meantime, the main train has reversed at Exeter St Davids and its four remaining triplets are propelled electrically to Newton Abbot. There the driving trailer temporarily detaches itself and retreats to a siding, allowing the electric outer suburban powered triplet which forms the off-peak service on the Paignton branch to couple onto the front of the train. The front triplet of the main train is then detached, and the two triplet combination (one powered and one trailer) departs as the train for Paignton.

The driving trailer then reattaches itself to the front of the main train, and its remaining three triplets depart for Plymouth. The high power to weight ratio of 16.7hp/tonne is now well suited to dealing with the steep gradients of south Devon.

At Plymouth the electric locomotive at the rear of the train removes the last coach triplet to a different platform. The remaining train now consists of a driving trailer and two triplets. An ex-HST diesel power couples onto the rear, and the combination is then propelled westwards towards Par.

A diesel power car forming an off-peak service from Tavistock arrives at Plymouth, and couples up to the triplet left in the platform. When this is done, the electric locomotive detaches itself and heads for the depot. In the meantime the diesel power car and triplet departs for Tavistock, complete with its through passengers.

The remaining train of two triplets on the main line is now within the capabilities of the ex-HST power car, and further relief will come at Par. As this train is proceeding down the main line, a lightly loaded diesel power car is scuttling by itself from Newquay to Par. It arrives at Par first.

After the main train arrives in the down platform at Par, it splits in half. The rear triplet is moved by the ex-HST power car to couple onto the diesel power car from Newquay. Next the ex-HST power car detaches itself and rejoins what is left of the main train.

The final main train combination of driving trailer, one coach triplet and ex-HST power car can cope well with the difficult remaining gradients and curves of the line to Penzance. It also has boost power from the driving trailer, and battery back up if things go wrong on this remote stretch of line. In the meantime, the diesel power car and triplet detached at Par head for Newquay with those through passengers.

In this way, the six sections of the original train are sent to six different destinations, using the traction resources local to the various branch lines with no special equipment or facilities. Of course on the return journey the whole process happens in reverse, with driving cabs judiciously placed to be in the front of the propelled sections of trains before they are combined together again.

This rather extreme example of train splitting illustrates the great flexibility of the concept. If it is necessary to move rolling stock around the network, it can often be done by attaching it to scheduled services heading in the right direction, reducing the need for special empty stock movements. A network-wide rolling stock approach can lead to greater overall efficiency: as mentioned already there is some scope for sharing resources between commuter and long-distance businesses with mutually beneficial results. Also, during the winter demand on many rural routes will be low, so coaches can be borrowed then by the cross country or inter-city businesses to give coverage for special events or maintenance work. Conversely, at the height of the holiday season business travel will reduce and coaches can be transferred to popular scenic lines.

By having a compatible set of vehicles as described in this strategy, the flexibility once available to passenger train operators in the steam era half a century ago can be restored, in an enhanced modern form. Remember, though: achieving such advantages depends on BOVRIL, not COCOA. Cheers!

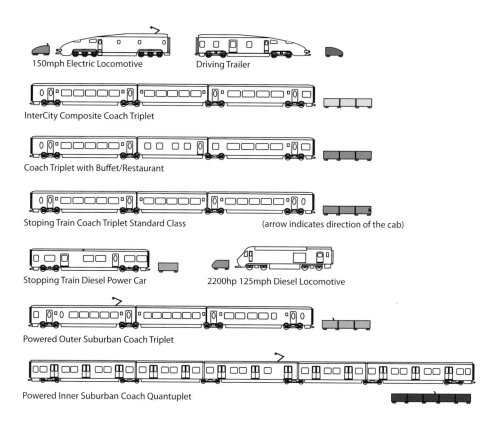

150mph Electric Locomotive   Driving Trailer

InterCity Composite Coach Triplet

Coach Triplet with Buffet/Restaurant

Stoping Train Coach Triplet Standard Class   (arrow indicates direction of the cab)

Stopping Train Diesel Power Car   2200hp 125mph Diesel Locomotive

Powered Outer Suburban Coach Triplet

Powered Inner Suburban Coach Quantuplet

Beyond the HST   A proposed design strategy for future trains in Britain

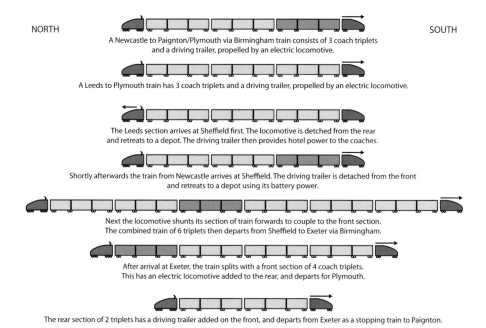

NORTH

SOUTH

A Newcastle to Paignton/Plymouth via Birmingham train consists of 3 coach triplets
and a driving trailer, propelled by an electric locomotive.

A Leeds to Plymouth train has 3 coach triplets and a driving trailer, propelled by an electric locomotive.

The Leeds section arrives at Sheffield first. The locomotive is detched from the rear
and retreats to a depot. The driving trailer then provides hotel power to the coaches.

Shortly afterwards the train from Newcastle arrives at Sheffield. The driving trailer is detached from the front
and retreats to a depot using its battery power.

Next the locomotive shunts its section of train forwards to couple to the front section.
The combined train of 6 triplets then departs from Sheffield to Exeter via Birmingham.

After arrival at Exeter, the train splits with a front section of 4 coach triplets.
This has an electric locomotive added to the rear, and departs for Plymouth.

The rear section of 2 triplets has a driving trailer added on the front, and departs from Exeter as a stopping train to Paignton.

Figure 21: *Train formations Newcastle/Leeds to Paignton/Plymouth*

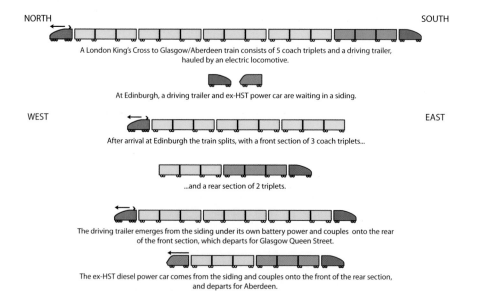

NORTH

SOUTH

A London King's Cross to Glasgow/Aberdeen train consists of 5 coach triplets and a driving trailer,
hauled by an electric locomotive.

At Edinburgh, a driving trailer and ex-HST power car are waiting in a siding.

WEST

EAST

After arrival at Edinburgh the train splits, with a front section of 3 coach triplets...

...and a rear section of 2 triplets.

The driving trailer emerges from the siding under its own battery power and couples onto the rear
of the front section, which departs for Glasgow Queen Street.

The ex-HST diesel power car comes from the siding and couples onto the front of the rear section,
and departs for Aberdeen.

Figure 22: *Train formations London to Glasgow/Aberdeen*

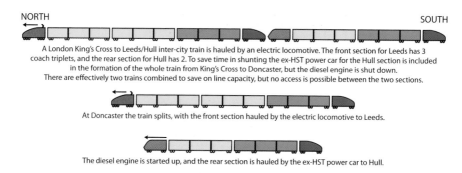

NORTH   SOUTH

A London King's Cross to Leeds/Hull inter-city train is hauled by an electric locomotive. The front section for Leeds has 3
coach triplets, and the rear section for Hull has 2. To save time in shunting the ex-HST power car for the Hull section is included
in the formation of the whole train from King's Cross to Doncaster, but the diesel engine is shut down.
There are effectively two trains combined to save on line capacity, but no access is possible between the two sections.

At Doncaster the train splits, with the front section hauled by the electric locomotive to Leeds.

The diesel engine is started up, and the rear section is hauled by the ex-HST power car to Hull.

Figure 23: *Train formations London to Leeds/Hull*

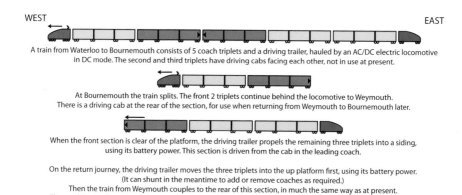

WEST   EAST

A train from Waterloo to Bournemouth consists of 5 coach triplets and a driving trailer, hauled by an AC/DC electric locomotive
in DC mode. The second and third triplets have driving cabs facing each other, not in use at present.

At Bournemouth the train splits. The front 2 triplets continue behind the locomotive to Weymouth.
There is a driving cab at the rear of the section, for use when returning from Weymouth to Bournemouth later.

When the front section is clear of the platform, the driving trailer propels the remaining three triplets into a siding,
using its battery power. This section is driven from the cab in the leading coach.

On the return journey, the driving trailer moves the three triplets into the up platform first, using its battery power.
(It can shunt in the meantime to add or remove coaches as required.)
Then the train from Weymouth couples to the rear of this section, in much the same way as at present.
The combined train, with the driving trailer now leading, is propelled by the locomotive back to London Waterloo.

Figure 24: *Train formations London to Weymouth*

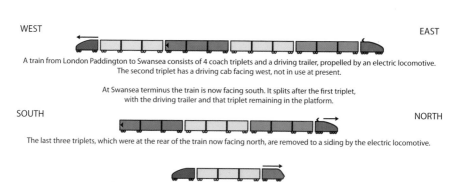

WEST   EAST

A train from London Paddington to Swansea consists of 4 coach triplets and a driving trailer, propelled by an electric locomotive.
The second triplet has a driving cab facing west, not in use at present.

At Swansea terminus the train is now facing south. It splits after the first triplet,
with the driving trailer and that triplet remaining in the platform.

SOUTH   NORTH

The last three triplets, which were at the rear of the train now facing north, are removed to a siding by the electric locomotive.

An ex-HST diesel power car then attaches to the north end of the train in the platform, which departs for Pembroke Dock.

On the return journey, the section from West Wales arrives in the platform first, propelled by the ex-HST power car. The power car is
then detached and retreats to a siding. Next the main part of the train is propelled from its siding by the electric locomotive, driven
from the cab in the leading coach, to join the West Wales section in the platform.
Finally the combined train reverses northwards, heading back to London Paddington.

Figure 25: *Train formations London to Swansea/Pembroke Dock*

Beyond the HST   A proposed design strategy for future trains in Britain

NORTH   SOUTH

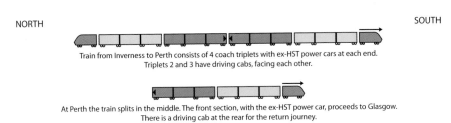

Train from Inverness to Perth consists of 4 coach triplets with ex-HST power cars at each end.
Triplets 2 and 3 have driving cabs, facing each other.

At Perth the train splits in the middle. The front section, with the ex-HST power car, proceeds to Glasgow.
There is a driving cab at the rear for the return journey.

The rear section then continues to Edinburgh, driven from the cab in the leading coach triplet. On the return journey,
the ex-HST power car will be at the front.

On the return journey, the portion from Edinburgh arrives at Perth first and then the rear section from Glasgow couples onto it
before the whole train continues to Inverness.

Figure 26: *Train formations Inverness to Glasgow/Edinburgh*

WEST   EAST

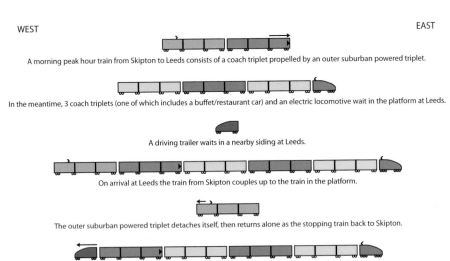

A morning peak hour train from Skipton to Leeds consists of a coach triplet propelled by an outer suburban powered triplet.

In the meantime, 3 coach triplets (one of which includes a buffet/restaurant car) and an electric locomotive wait in the platform at Leeds.

A driving trailer waits in a nearby siding at Leeds.

On arrival at Leeds the train from Skipton couples up to the train in the platform.

The outer suburban powered triplet detaches itself, then returns alone as the stopping train back to Skipton.

The driving trailer moves from the siding using its battery power and couples onto the front of the train in the platform.

The train (complete with its through passengers from Skipton) then departs from Leeds as an inter-city train to London,
propelled by the locomotive.

Figure 27: *Train formations Skipton and Leeds to London*

WEST   EAST

A morning peak hour stopping train from Lowestoft to Norwich consists of a single coach triplet propelled by a diesel power car. There is a cab in the leading coach.

In the meantime, another coach triplet and ex-HST diesel power car wait in the platform at Norwich.

A driving trailer waits in a nearby siding at Norwich.

On arrival at Norwich the train from Lowestoft couples up to the train in the platform.

The diesel power car detaches itself, then returns alone as the stopping train to Lowestoft.

The driving trailer moves from the siding using its battery power and couples onto the front of the train in the platform.

The train (complete with its through passengers from Lowestoft) then departs from Norwich as a cross country train to Birmingham, propelled by the ex-HST power car.

Figure 28: *Train formations Lowestoft and Norwich to Birmingham*

Figure 29: *Train formation Matlock – Derby – Nottingham – Lincoln*

WEST   EAST

A London Waterloo to Exeter/Barnstaple/Plymouth/Newquay/Penzance train consists of 6 coach triplets and a driving trailer, hauled by an AC/DC electric locomotive.

At Exeter Central the train divides into a front portion of 4 coach triplets...

...and a rear portion of 2 triplets. This rear section is shunted by the driving trailer under battery power to a different platform.

A diesel power car, which has arrived from Barnstaple as an off peak stopping train, attaches to the west end of this section. The driving trailer is then detached, and returns to the main train. The main train of 4 coach triplets then departs for Exeter St David's.

Next another diesel power car arrives at Exeter Central from Exmouth and attaches to the east end of the section. The two triplets then split; the resulting trains head westwards to Barnstaple and eastwards to Exmouth respectively, complete with their through passengers from London.

After reversal at Exeter St David's, the main train heads westward again, with the driving trailer now leading and propelled by the electric locomotive.

Figure 30a: *Train formations London Waterloo to West Country*

Beyond the HST   A proposed design strategy for future trains in Britain

WEST   EAST

On arrival at Newton Abbot, the driving trailer is temporarily detached from the front of the train and retreats to a siding. An electric outer suburban triplet, which forms the off peak service train on the Paignton branch, is attached to the front of the train in its place.

The train then splits, and the outer suburban triplet hauls the first coach triplet from the main train to Paignton, complete with its through passengers.

The driving trailer rejoins the remaining 3 triplets of the main train and departs westwards from Newton Abbot for Plymouth.

After arriving at Plymouth, the train splits again and the rear triplet is shunted to a different platform by the electric locomotive. A diesel power car from Tavistock joins that section at the west end.

The electric locomotive then heads off to the depot, and the diesel power car hauls the coach triplet with its through passengers as a stopping train from Plymough to Tavistock.

Meanwhile an ex-HST diesel power car is attached to the rear of the remaining 2 coach triplets at Plymouth and heads westward on the main line to Par.

After arriving at Par, the train splits and the rear coach triplet is shunted so that it joins a diesel power car which has arrived from Newquay.

The ex-HST power car is detached, and the diesel power car hauls the coach triplet and its passengers to Newquay.

The ex-HST power car rejoins the remaining coach triplet, and propels it to Penzance.

Figure 30b: *Train formations London Waterloo to West Country*

Chapter 17

Sleeping car services

At present, only a limited number of sleeping car services remain, from London to Scotland and the West Country. This contrasts with the situation a couple of decades ago, where sleeping cars could be taken in the south coast or north east, and even locally within Scotland.

Part of the reason for the decline is that improved daytime speeds on a few routes made the provision of sleeping car services less necessary. Also, sleeping cars have often been perceived as unattractive and old-fashioned, with cramped accommodation and either expensive or a bit questionable through having to share compartments with strangers. A major factor, however, has been related to technology: sleeping car services have remained locomotive-hauled, whereas daytime services have mostly changed to different kinds of train. This has meant that sleeping car services have become 'special', with different kinds of traction only used at night.

These factors have constrained the economics of sleeping car services, making them marginally viable except for the heavier flows between distant big cities. A few remain to small places such as Fort William, surviving due to political pressure, difficult road access and the possibilities of hitching a lift on a more popular sleeper train route for part of the journey.

With the BOVRIL rolling stock design philosophy, however, these technical constraints can be removed. Sleeping cars just become coaches like any other coaches, and can be hauled in traffic by any type of traction described in this strategy. It is not necessary to have special 'sleeping car locomotives', and since services operate at night there is usually plenty of traction available locally which would otherwise lie idle in depots.

For long-distance trunk routes the sleeping cars can be run in dedicated sleeper-only services as now, or combined with normal inter-city coaches, depending on the demand for different types of accommodation. In addition to the electric and diesel locomotives used on inter-city and cross country trains, sleeping cars can also be hauled by electric outer suburban triplets, inner suburban quintuplets and the diesel power cars used for stopping trains. This gives the flexibility to provide sleeping car services to many smaller places with low demand, by making use of the traction resources already available locally.

Usually, sleeping cars will be swapped between trains during the night as they run together on core routes or separately on local trains. Consequently, the current idea of several sleeping cars coupled to a seating 'lounge' car is not ideal; either the lounge cars disappear when trains are split or more have to be found for the local journeys. To give an attractive service, it is necessary to have both seating and sleeping accommodation for overnight passengers, allowing meals to be taken in comfort (either in the evening or at breakfast) and retiring to bed when ready to do so.

A proposed design for a sleeping car triplet is shown in *Figure 32*. This uses the standard coach structure to provide twelve sleeping compartments and twelve seats at tables, together with three toilets and a small kitchen / pantry. It is effectively a self-contained small hotel on wheels, manageable by one attendant. Consequently, one sleeping coach triplet can be coupled to a diesel power car if necessary to provide a low demand sleeping facility to a remote branch line. Since this might be a common application, it is proposed that all sleeping car triplets would be provided with driving cabs, so that they can be propelled by whatever traction is available if necessary. This gives full flexibility for all kinds of services.

In common with small hotels, not all the rooms are the same and they could command different prices. Five of the twelve are equipped with showers, located above the wheel boxes (it is necessary to step up into them; otherwise the usual low floor is maintained). In the centre coach, a partition wall can fold up against one of the access doors to make a spacious twin room when necessary. En suite toilets are not provided, due to the desirability of maintaining the same spacing as normal coaches for retention tank disposal at depots; but three toilets are available for twelve passengers, which should be ample.

Given the low density of provision (two conventional sleeping cars would provide twenty-four compartments in the same length) this kind of sleeper service would not be cheap. It would be of a much higher standard than current sleepers though, and could be cost-effective for the customer compared with the alternative of long-distance day travel and staying overnight in a reasonable hotel. Given appropriate timings and a captive market for evening meals, combined dinner / bed / breakfast / travel deals should allow a competitive and viable business model to be created in the right environment.

Since sleeper services do not normally need to be especially fast, lower power to weight ratios will do and trains can be longer than usual for a given type of traction unit. A standard stopping train diesel power car is designed to provide sufficient hotel power for two coach triplets, which could be sleepers. Such a combination would only have a nominal 3.6hp/tonne of traction capability, which is low but adequate for plodding along a flat branch line at a medium speed. Battery boost is available as usual for improvements in acceleration or help with climbing short gradients.

Of course, more power cars can be added to the train as necessary, in any convenient order. As with normal coaches, sleeping cars can go at up to 150mph behind inter-city electric locomotives, 125mph with diesel locomotives or ex-HST power cars, 100mph with stopping train diesel power cars or outer suburban electric triplets, or 75mph with inner suburban electric quintuplets. All forms of traction provide sufficient hotel power for at least two sleeper triplets per traction unit, and mixed combinations of traction units can be coupled together too.

With a single sleeping car triplet, the minimum capacity train on a remote branch line having twenty-eight seats in the power car and twelve sleeping passengers would be a useful strategic overnight public service for many small places. When the night journey is complete, the diesel power car is then in the right place to haul a normal coach triplet for a morning train service from such a terminus. In many cases, this would avoid the need for a local depot, as the power car could be serviced more centrally; only the standard coach triplet (a low-tech vehicle needing little servicing) would remain at the remote location overnight.

By making use of these synergies between services, and not attempting to compartmentalise them into separate competing businesses, it ought to be possible to make overnight services more viable commercially assuming a supportive regulatory environment. Places like Whitby, Whitehaven, Barrow in Furness, Hartlepool, Aberystwyth, Falmouth, Newquay, Wick and Thurso might be able to justify overnight services using this approach.

The same shunting techniques described in the previous chapter can be used for sleeping car services. As an example, consider a **London Euston to Stirling / Perth / Oban / Fort William** overnight service as shown in *Figure 31*. This starts from London with an electric locomotive, six sleeping car triplets and a driving trailer. At Mossend (north of Motherwell) the electric locomotive is detached and two stopping train diesel power cars are coupled to the front instead. The train splits in the middle, and the two diesel power cars with three triplets head off for Cowlairs and the West Highland line. An ex-HST diesel power car couples to the remaining three triplets and driving trailer and heads for Larbert and the north.

The West Highland section continues to Crianlarich, where the front diesel power car is detached and shunts around to couple on the rear. The train then splits, the front two triplets being hauled to Fort William and the rear triplet propelled to Oban. These two locations then have diesel power cars available to haul morning train services to Glasgow.

In the meantime, the other section proceeds to Stirling where the rear triplet is detached. Using battery power the driving trailer shunts this into a platform, where it remains. There is sufficient battery charge available in the driving trailer to keep the lights and air-conditioning going on this single triplet (and to power the cooker for cooked breakfasts!) until the sleeping car passengers leave at Stirling at a reasonable hour in the morning. Meanwhile, the ex-HST diesel power car has proceeded to Perth with the front two sleeping car triplets, and remains there in a platform, providing power until it is time for the passengers to leave.

As well as conventional scheduled sleeping car services, the vehicle strategy is well suited to the provision of 'on-demand' overnight services for excursions or special events. There should also be scope to reintroduce non-London sleeping car services, for example between the south coast or West Country and Scotland.

Further opportunities might be overnight services to and from Ashford to connect with international trains, and services to Fishguard, Holyhead and Stranraer connecting with ferries to Ireland. It might be possible to use the same vehicles on through services via the Channel Tunnel to European destinations too, if the political, technical and regulatory hurdles can be overcome.

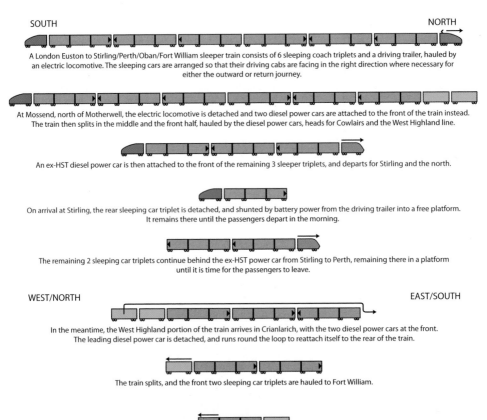

SOUTH   NORTH

A London Euston to Stirling/Perth/Oban/Fort William sleeper train consists of 6 sleeping coach triplets and a driving trailer, hauled by an electric locomotive. The sleeping cars are arranged so that their driving cabs are facing in the right direction where necessary for either the outward or return journey.

At Mossend, north of Motherwell, the electric locomotive is detached and two diesel power cars are attached to the front of the train instead. The train then splits in the middle and the front half, hauled by the diesel power cars, heads for Cowlairs and the West Highland line.

An ex-HST diesel power car is then attached to the front of the remaining 3 sleeper triplets, and departs for Stirling and the north.

On arrival at Stirling, the rear sleeping car triplet is detached, and shunted by battery power from the driving trailer into a free platform. It remains there until the passengers depart in the morning.

The remaining 2 sleeping car triplets continue behind the ex-HST power car from Stirling to Perth, remaining there in a platform until it is time for the passengers to leave.

WEST/NORTH   EAST/SOUTH

In the meantime, the West Highland portion of the train arrives in Crianlarich, with the two diesel power cars at the front. The leading diesel power car is detached, and runs round the loop to reattach itself to the rear of the train.

The train splits, and the front two sleeping car triplets are hauled to Fort William.

Finally the rear sleeping car triplet is propelled from Crianlarich to Oban.

Figure 31: *Sleeping car train formations London to Stirling/Perth/Oban/Fort William*

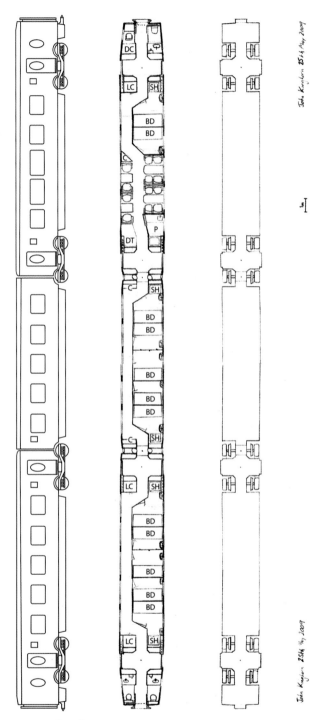

Figure 32: *Sleeping car coach triplet*
BD bed SH shower C cupboard LC linen cupboard
P pantry/kitchen DT display table DC driving cab

153

Chapter 18

Special trains and adapting vehicles

In addition to the scheduled seating and sleeping services described above, some other kinds of train need to be considered and solutions provided within the overall rolling stock strategy. This includes the provision of new vehicles and the adaptation of existing ones, for facilities available now or which might be introduced in the future.

Vans

A useful vehicle might be the general purpose van. This could be used for the conveyance of unaccompanied luggage, parcels, newspapers, and general merchandise. Of course at present such traffic does not exist on passenger trains, but is organisationally strictly separated into the freight sector run by different companies. Nevertheless, a comprehensive national network of passenger trains traversing the country at high speeds day and night is a useful resource, and future generations of railway managers might be able to recreate a premium parcels service of some kind using passenger trains, taking advantage of synergies with the passenger business to keep costs down.

In the early stages of such a business the van space available in driving trailers, electric outer suburban triplets and diesel power cars might be adequate, but if the strategy is successful, additional capacity will be needed. Single vans, 21m long with the same 14m bogie spacing and body profile as the coaches, could be produced to accommodate expanding business of this kind in a flexible way. They would be designed to the usual standards with the same couplings and bogies as the passenger coaches, with the same 150mph maximum speed.

The black box on the train information bus in the van would be simple, just describing the van's weight and storage area, with no facilities to be controlled or sensed except confirmation that access doors are closed and locked. The same low floor design as the coaches would be used for level access from platforms in the middle of the vehicle, with higher floor sections over the bogies and slopes leading to them. Wide vertical roller shutter doors in the centre of each van would give access to the unrestricted storage space. The ends would have the standard corridor connections to permit access through the train if required, and there would be the usual sliding lockable corridor doors.

For higher capacity a van triplet 50m long could be considered. This would be an adaptation of the standard coach triplet vehicle structure, again with level access from platforms in the centre of each coach, and slopes to higher floor levels above the bogies. In this case, the higher floor levels would be continued across the articulation points, and the junction between vehicle bodies at those points would be (almost) the full width of the vehicle. This would allow easy loading of the vehicles from the ends, permitting loading equipment to pass between those vans if necessary.

Exactly the same vehicles could be used as car carriers if it is decided to revive long-distance motorail services, with the vans included in overnight passenger services to ensure that cars and drivers end up in the same place at the same time. They would also be useful for carrying large numbers of bicycles for big special events when the demand exceeds the usual provision.

Such vehicles would also be useful for carrying engineering equipment or stores, either for work on the line or to transfer them between depots without the need for special trains.

Adapting existing coaches

It might be necessary to mix vehicles in trains for a period, using both old and new designs. This is possible to a limited extent.

Since the new train strategy uses essentially the same control, hotel power and braking standards as the HST, coaches from redundant HSTs could be adapted to work together with the new vehicle designs. New couplings would be needed at the outer ends of the old coach formation, below the existing couplers or coupling bars. Additional through wiring for the new facilities between couplers would have to be added.

If the older coaches were only going to be used for a limited period, the corresponding black boxes on the train information bus could be omitted and their data (in terms of weight especially) entered manually into the locomotive terminal to give the correct operating dynamics. There are no seat reservation displays in those coaches anyway, so the old method of paper tickets would be retained.

Another issue is the different floor heights. Without modification, the old coach would present a step up of about 30cm at the corridor connection. A temporary slope

Plate 46: *Well designed electric locomotives can last for years, examples half a century old being found in service in some countries. The Class 90 was introduced in 1987, an 85 tonne 5000 hp machine with a top speed of 110 mph. Two examples are seen at London Liverpool Street on services from Norwich, a 115 mile route with 5 or 6 stops covered in under 2 hours at an average speed of 60 mph. Locomotives such as this can be readily adapted to haul the coaches of the proposed strategy, and would be very useful for all kinds of inter-city, cross country and commuter services for many years to come on routes where the lower top speed is acceptable.*

could be attached to the floor of the adjacent new coach to match the floor levels, although this would need to continue beyond the sliding door to the vehicle end to avoid a gap. This limitation, together with the complexity of arranging automatic uncoupling facilities in the old coach, would probably mean a fixed formation of older coaches in traffic without the new flexibility to change train lengths easily. This might be perfectly acceptable in some situations; it is no worse than at present.

Given the complexities of different control systems, couplers fouling the end of the new design, different hotel power standards, etc., it is probably not worth attempting to adapt other types of existing coaches to match the proposed new coach designs.

Adapting existing locomotives

It may be desirable to haul the new coaches with existing locomotives, either for regular service or on special occasions. This can be done without too much difficulty.

Plate 47: *Any type of locomotive can be adapted to haul the coaches of the proposed strategy. It needs couplers to the new standard, an interface unit for the control signals and air braking capability. If the locomotive does not provide hotel power, this can be arranged by including a driving trailer or diesel power car in the train formation. Even steam locomotives could be adapted, such as this 1950s standard 2-6-4 tank engine arriving at Corfe Castle on the Swanage Railway. Through coaches to Swanage from London Waterloo, steam hauled from Wareham, would be possible again with such a facility.*

The first essential is to provide couplers to the new standard at the lower level. Not all its facilities need be implemented, however. Of course, the braking system must be compatible, and if it is desired to propel the train then the traction control system must be compatible too. If not, a simpler interface can be provided which just enables the train to act as a straightforward conventional trailing load.

Since many locomotives provide different standards of hotel power to that used in the new coaches, if they provide hotel power at all, this might seem to be a serious difficulty. However, this can be solved by including the right vehicles in the train. As already noted, a driving trailer can provide hotel power, derived from its storage battery. This in turn is charged from its traction motors used as generators in regenerative braking. However, it is also possible to choose to apply regenerative braking force in the driving trailer purely for the purpose of charging the battery, even when the intention is not to decelerate the train or restrict its speed on a downwards gradient.

The trick, then, is to provide an interface on the old locomotive which (via the train information bus) monitors the state of the battery charge and if it falls below a certain

157

threshold partially applies the brakes. This is sufficient to bring regenerative braking from the driving trailer into action, but not enough to apply the train disc brakes. Consequently, the batteries are kept charged, enough to power the hotel bus from the driving trailer and keep the train lights and air-conditioning going indefinitely.

This method of applying extra traction force from the locomotive via the rails to the driving trailer to generate power to drive the train facilities may seem a roundabout way of doing it, but it is very flexible and not particularly inefficient. It can be considered as a large scale version of the old method of driving train lights from dynamos mounted on the coaches.

Consequently, any type of locomotive can be adapted to haul the new coaches, using a black box to interface its controls to the new standard, together with a new coupler. This is possible regardless of whether the locomotive is electric, diesel, LPG, gas turbine, steam or any other form of traction which might come in future. With a little extra work, the new steam locomotive Tornado can haul the new coaches without difficulty. Of course some traction capability is 'stolen' to provide hotel power, but manual intervention can arrange battery charging at appropriate times if necessary, not when struggling with a heavy train up a steep gradient!

Another alternative is to include a diesel power car in the formation instead of a driving trailer, and use that to provide hotel power. If the diesel power car does not have to provide traction, it has enough capacity to power a long train in principle. However, the current capability of its hotel power inverter will be a limitation, so the technique would be restricted to shorter trains with two triplets per power car. More power cars could be added if necessary, but then it would be questionable why another locomotive is providing traction at all. This could occur, however, when it is convenient to move a locomotive in a train without a separate light engine movement, or for heritage traction in an enthusiasts' special train.

Of course, if the old locomotive does provide hotel power, a more conventional and better solution would be to add an inverter or transformer to provide AC hotel power according to the new standard.

Such adaptations will allow many existing assets to continue making a valuable contribution to the requirements of the network, without the need to scrap all the old stuff when new trains are introduced. In particular, several existing electric locomotive types could have many years of useful service yet in powering the new coaches on routes where their lower top speeds are not a serious limitation.

Chapter 19

Review

The proposed train strategy has now been described, hopefully in sufficient detail to get a clear idea of the concept and some key design parameters. It is time to review whether the proposal meets the intended objectives, and what the performance and cost implications might be.

Electric inter-city trains

First of all, consider the electric inter-city train. This is particularly critical to get right, as the intention is to electrify all busy inter-city routes in the longer term. Interim solutions may be workable with diesel traction, but the electric solution needs to be as optimum as possible as it will have a profound effect on the success of the British railway network for the next half-century.

The objectives were:

- Maximum speed of 150mph.
- High passenger comfort (low noise and vibration, good view etc.).
- Good space per seat (width and spacing).
- Ease of access (good door positions and floors level with platforms).
- Flexibility to alter capacity to demand.
- Energy efficiency consistent with sufficient performance.
- Low running costs consistent with sufficient performance.
- Easy adaptation between electric and diesel operation.

The maximum speed of 150mph does seem achievable, subject to confirmation of acceptable track wear, which depends in turn on suspension design, particularly in the six axle locomotive. Also, there needs to be confirmation that the improved streamlining will be sufficient to allow 150mph with the intended 6,000hp installed power. If not, maybe the power needs to increase a little, but the approach should still be viable.

High passenger comfort is definitely achieved. The coaches are all unpowered trailers, and there are no motors or drives in them to cause noise and vibration. Suspensions can be compliant for a smooth ride as there are no traction forces in the coaches and braking forces are limited. Windows are placed to give a good view from all seats.

A spacious layout is achieved, with a significantly wider coach body and generous seat pitches to fit the larger passengers of today and the future. More headroom is available in corridors and door openings for taller people.

Good access is provided. Coach floors are level with platforms and there are no steps. Doors are spaced evenly throughout the train and there are wide vestibules and aisles to facilitate rapid loading and unloading.

There is excellent flexibility to alter capacity to demand, with a wide range of options to suit particular requirements. Formations can easily be changed through the day anywhere on the network, with or without passengers being present. Shunting facilities are available at both ends of the train at all times. Different kinds of vehicles, such as restaurant or sleeping cars, can be added or removed easily according to specific needs. In off-peak periods shorter train formations can give significantly improved acceleration and braking performance, resulting in faster journeys than those achievable with a fixed formation train.

Energy efficiency should be good for a train having such performance. For high speed long-distance services, good streamlining is provided to minimise air resistance, the most significant factor. For slower services with more frequent stops, regenerative braking allows kinetic energy to be recovered to reduce energy consumption.

Maintenance costs should be moderate and easy to manage due to the concentration of complex systems on the locomotive and driving trailer, with simple low maintenance coaches. If necessary, trains can be split to fit existing maintenance facilities with no need for new depots. Brake wear is limited through the use of regenerative braking. There are fewer powered axles than a train using distributed power, and consequently there are fewer traction motors and drives to maintain, which should reduce costs.

As the concept is a locomotive-hauled train, it is easy to change between electric and diesel traction. It is expected that existing diesel locomotive designs will be used, without the need for any new ones. This avoids unnecessary expenditure on assets having increasingly limited application as electrification progresses.

In summary, all the objectives have been achieved, with a few items subject to confirmation through more detailed study. However, how does the new design concept compare with other solutions?

At the time of writing, the leading contender for a future electric inter-city train is the ten-car SET (Super Express Train) promoted by the DfT. Table 3 compares SET with the new design electric inter-city train proposed here. The example shown has five triplets; this is the nearest in length to the ten-car SET. All figures in the table are approximate, but they should be close enough for some reasonable conclusions to be drawn.

	New Proposal	SET
Formation	Co-Co locomotive Five unpowered coach triplets Driving trailer	Driving trailer Five powered coaches Three unpowered coaches Driving trailer
Length (m)	290	260
Seats (low density)	479	649
Seats (high density)	780	740
Weight (t)	500	412
Top speed (mph)	150	140
Installed power (hp)	6,000	5,360
Powered axles	10	20
Unpowered axles	40	20
Power to weight ratio (hp/t)	12	13
Axle loads (t)	15 (x10) 9 (x40)	12.2 (x4) 11 (x20) 8 (x16)
Adhesive weight % for traction	18	53
Driving cabs	2	2
Powered coaches	0	5
Unpowered coaches	15	5
Passenger doors	19	18
Average seats per door	25	36
Standard toilets	10	10
Wheelchair access toilets	5	2
Average seats per toilet	32	54
Wheelchair spaces	5	?

	New Proposal	SET
Formation	Co-Co locomotive Five unpowered coach triplets Driving trailer	Driving trailer Five powered coaches Three unpowered coaches Driving trailer
Bicycle storage area (sq. m)	9	?
Regenerative braking	Yes	Yes
Adhesive weight % for regenerative braking	30	53
Battery traction boost	Yes	Yes
Hotel power maintenance	Yes	Yes
Move without supply	Yes	Yes
Alter formation in traffic	Yes	No
Traction motors	6 x 1000hp 4 x 500hp	20 x 270hp
Traction inverters	8	5
Drives	10	20
Traction power bus line	No	Yes
High voltage bus line	No	Yes

Table 3
Electric inter-city trains compared

Regarding journey times, the two trains have rather different characteristics. The SET has a much higher adhesive weight percentage for traction, and this will allow higher acceleration at very low speeds where adhesion is the limit. On the other hand, power will become the constraint quite quickly so from medium speeds upwards either solution has adequate adhesion for the power available. The new proposal has a slightly lower power to weight ratio, but it has better streamlining which will improve acceleration at high speeds by reducing air resistance. It also has a higher top speed. So on a short-distance run SET will win, but on a longer distance journey, when high speeds are involved, the proposed new train will catch up and overtake. Overall there is probably not much difference between the schedules possible for typical medium-distance inter-city journeys on either train when the formations in the table are chosen.

With the new proposal, however, it is possible to choose a shorter formation with higher acceleration and braking capability. For example, a four-triplet train has a higher power to weight ratio than SET (14hp/tonne) and about 400 seats, so it will give shorter journey times when the lower capacity is acceptable. Shorter trains of three or fewer triplets will be faster still. Formations can be altered throughout the day to match demand, and some very fast off-peak schedules should be possible even when there are frequent stops. Also, special shorter high speed premium services can be run during the day if the journey time reductions are commercially worthwhile on a particular route. There is great flexibility to choose different options, which are not available with SET.

Regarding energy efficiency, the SET has a significantly higher adhesive weight percentage for regenerative braking, but at the higher speeds when most energy can be recovered adhesion is adequate in both cases. Consequently, there will not be a great difference in the amount of energy retrieved, and in any case a typical inter-city journey will have relatively few braking periods. This means that even excellent regenerative braking will have limited impact on the overall energy consumption for a long-distance service with a straight route and few stops. Both trains are comparable regarding energy recovery, with SET rather better. On the other hand, the improved streamlining of the new proposal may make a significant impact in saving energy at high speeds, outweighing the energy saved through regenerative braking. Simulations would need to be done to find out how much energy is consumed by the two solutions, and it will vary depending on the route characteristics and service patterns. The new proposal will be better at high speed, and SET better at lower speeds. Overall there will probably be little to choose between the two solutions in terms of energy efficiency for typical journey patterns.

Regarding seating capacity, the figures in the table for 'low density' and 'high density' reflect the 'inter-city' and 'commuter' seating layouts respectively. For the new proposal it is assumed that one of the five triplets has a buffet / restaurant car. In the 'low density' inter-city application, the absurdly high proposed SET seating capacity no doubt reflects the desire to cram in as many people as possible to reduce the cost per seat. However, this is an area where too high 'efficiency' will produce cramped and uncomfortable travelling conditions, which will drive away passengers; not what is needed. The level proposed for SET means on average one toilet for every fifty-four seats, which is surely unacceptable for long journeys of several hours on an inter-city train. The average of one access door per thirty-six seats will mean conventionally slow loading and unloading times too.

For the 'high density' commuter seating, the new proposal has a slightly higher capacity than SET. This reflects the possibility of introducing two-plus-three seating with a reasonable level of comfort, given the wider coach body. In the commuter case it is assumed that a lower level of toilet provision would be acceptable for the generally shorter journey times.

Of course, either train can be fitted with seating of any desired comfort, so in the inter-city case a more useful comparison is the train length available for seating. It is assumed that two-plus-two seating in standard class and two-plus-one in first class would be normal for this kind of train in either case, so it is the seating pitch which is critical for comfort. The new proposal has approximately 90% of the length of the SET available for seating; this reduction reflects the space occupied by the locomotive and driving trailer, and more generous space provision for toilets, luggage, vestibules and bicycle storage. Put another way, an SET with the same seating pitch as the new proposal would have about 530 seats instead of 649, which would result in a more reasonable forty-four seats per toilet on average; this is the real comparison that should be made.

If greater capacity is needed, the full-length new train using six triplets would have a seating capacity of 581 (assuming provision of a restaurant / buffet car). Its acceleration will be lower at low speeds, of course, but on long non-stop runs its improved streamlining and higher design speed will yield comparable or better journey times. In the extreme case, a six triplet new inter-city train having the level of seating densities proposed for SET could have 700 seats. Please don't do it: that approach would ruin the comfort of the concept completely!

Using the lower seating densities in both cases, the new proposal has about 15% fewer seats per door, which will slightly speed up loading and unloading compared to SET. A greater contribution to faster access will be made by the wider doors, aisles and vestibules, the absence of a step, more generous luggage space provision and the absence of internal doors, however. All these factors are significant influences in the times taken for passengers to alight and board trains, as observation of any well-loaded train at a station will verify. A reduction in loading times of at least 25% might be expected under average conditions: well worth having for an inter-city train if, for example, four-minute station stops become three-minute ones, and there are ten stops, then ten minutes are saved on the journey time without doing anything else.

The new proposal provides an intrinsically quieter and more vibration-free environment for the passengers, as none of the coaches are powered. Ride quality will be better too due to the more compliant suspensions.

Most of the additional features and performance arising from the use of rechargeable batteries are the same for both trains. The degree of acceleration boost, power supply backup and movement in case of power failure is more or less the same for both trains, being dependent on the installed battery capacity decided on which is a question of cost. Similar lengths of coaches need to be supplied with lighting and air-conditioning, using the same power, so backup times will be the same for the same battery cost.

The new proposal has an advantage in terms of safety, in that the batteries are located in the centre of the robustly constructed driving trailer and away from passenger seating areas. Lithium ion batteries are generally safe after the manufacturing improvements of recent years, but in this application they contain considerable amounts of energy, which, if released through equipment failure or accident, has the potential for causing significant fires or explosions. Naturally, appropriate electrical and mechanical protection measures will be taken, but it is still a good idea to keep them away from passenger areas if possible.

Should it be decided (unwisely in the author's opinion) that a diesel donkey engine is necessary for backup power, either train concept can accommodate it. The new proposal has an advantage in this case; locating the donkey engine in the driving trailer keeps its fuel, noise and pollution away from the passenger areas and simplifies maintenance by having it in a detachable vehicle which could be fuelled and serviced separately from the main train if convenient.

A major advantage of the new concept compared with SET is the ability to change train formations in traffic, with the driving trailer acting as a kind of 'built-in shunting engine' to give maximum flexibility. Within the limits of maximum train length any type of coaches can be added or removed, from either end of the train. Such flexibility is simply not possible with SET, as its traction and control resources are not designed to operate independently: they need to act together as a whole. For example, the driving trailers at either end of the train cannot move by themselves, as they have no traction motors. The formations of SETs can be changed a little within the constraints in depots to fit the general demands of different routes, but it is not possible to change train lengths throughout the day in traffic to match demand. If it could be done, there would be no need for the 'hybrid' SET version, with a diesel generator car at one end and a transformer car at the other.

Regarding the capital costs of the two train concepts, consider the various key components.

The new proposal has half the number of traction motors compared with SET although they are higher power; probably this will give some cost saving. On the other hand, the new proposal has more traction inverters and needs higher performance adhesion control systems, so there will be some extra cost there. There are the same number of cabs and controls for both trains, and roughly the same total traction and regenerative braking power requirements overall. The new proposal has one big transformer instead of SET's two smaller ones; probably a bit cheaper. Also, there is no need for either a traction power bus or a high voltage bus in the new train, which will yield a cost saving (and safety benefits too). Battery capacity is the same for both trains. Overall, then, the electric traction components for the new proposal should be rather cheaper than SET.

Mechanically, the new train has a mixture of a few high-power, high-performance drives and suspensions in the locomotive and driving trailer, together with many simple unpowered suspensions in the coaches. The SET, on the other hand, has more medium-power drives and suspensions. Probably this balances out to give a similar cost for both trains.

From a material point of view, the articulated structure of the new proposal is more complex than the conventional coaches of SET. On the other hand, the short length and greater width and height of the new coaches makes the body structure inherently more rigid than the longer and narrower SET, so perhaps material and construction costs for the two solutions will not be very different in practice.

Given the above factors, a provisional conclusion before experts work out the real answers is that the new proposal should be less expensive than SET. That result is based on the assumption that any design can be built by any manufacturer, disregarding design costs, in a fully open competitive market; which is not the case in practice of course. A train builder offering a standard line of high speed electric multiple units will favour SET as it uses lots of the low-power traction components with which they are familiar. Equally, another manufacturer whose main business is in 21 tonne axle load Bo-Bo electric locomotives will probably not be very keen on making high speed 15 tonne axle load Co-Co ones. So at present these cost arguments are more theoretical than practical: nevertheless they give an indication of what manufacturing costs could be if it were decided to pursue the proposed design strategy, sufficient volumes were available to justify design costs and enterprising manufacturers (existing or new) were keen to support it.

Over the forty-year lifetime of the train, maintenance costs will often be more significant than manufacturing costs. Since the new proposal has fewer key mechanical components to maintain than SET (traction motors and drives) and can be split into sections easily to facilitate maintenance in existing depots rather than needing new ones, it seems probable that good design would allow significantly lower maintenance costs than SET.

In addition to the train itself, its cost impact on the network needs to be considered too. This will primarily relate to the level of track wear, and which of the two proposals is better in that respect is unclear. The new proposal has higher axle loads on the driven axles, but only half the number of them compared with SET. Non-driven axle loadings are lighter on both trains and may not have so much influence. Which solution is better for track wear? No doubt the answer critically depends on suspension design and component dynamics details, and will be hotly debated between the 'locomotive-hauled' and 'distributed power' protagonists. Acceleration and braking forces at high speeds will probably come into the picture too. From an outsider's point of view, it is hard to separate facts from spin to come to a real conclusion on this subject. Some erudite independent expert opinions in the public domain would help greatly. Perhaps, at the levels being considered here, there may not be very much difference in track costs between the new proposal and SET.

The overall simple conclusion is that the proposed electric inter-city train seems to offer superior performance and levels of comfort to SET, and far greater flexibility, at a somewhat lower cost.

The other main contender for the electric inter-city train is a conventional locomotive-hauled solution, adapted from standard European designs to the British loading gauge. Since there are no rechargeable batteries and only four traction motors and drives in the solution, and comparable costs for the other major components, this alternative should be cheaper to build than either the new proposal or SET. Design costs will be lower too as it is an adaptation of existing vehicles rather than anything radically new.

Comfort levels can be quite high, with unpowered coaches to give a noise- and vibration-free environment. Conventional coach designs will, however, be narrower than the articulated concept of the new proposal so seats cannot be quite so wide. Also, the conventional coach will have a high floor so there is no step-free access, and conventional end doors in long coaches will mean slower boarding times compared to the new proposal.

Running costs of the conventional train will be somewhat higher than the new proposal. Since the axle loadings on the Bo-Bo locomotive are substantially greater, this will result in greater track wear and increased track maintenance costs. Top speed on standard British track will be limited to 125mph; it would be possible to go faster (as in some other European countries) but that would probably require upgrading of the track on high speed sections. That is an option, but it would require high traffic levels to justify the cost. In addition, since the adhesive weight for regenerative braking is lower than the other solutions, energy efficiency will not be as good; so electricity consumption and brake wear will be higher. How much that increases running costs will depend on the route and service patterns. Over the lifetime of the train such increases in running costs may well outweigh the savings in capital costs. On the other hand, if performance is restricted to keep down such costs, less revenue might be generated from a slightly less attractive service.

Although much more flexible than SET, the conventional locomotive-hauled train does not have the advantages of the new proposal for changing train formations. Shunting can be carried out by the train locomotive or by using additional shunting engines located in strategic places. Although changing traction from electric to diesel is as easy as the new proposal, changes of train length may be a bit more complicated and time-consuming (or costly) to perform in traffic. There is also no backup for the lighting and air-conditioning power so it will fail briefly when sections of train are uncoupled from the locomotive. This is not a major problem, but is rather a disadvantage.

Also the conventional locomotive-hauled train has no backup for movement in case of major failure of the locomotive or its power supply. Rescue in these circumstances depends on the arrival of another locomotive.

Weighing up the various factors for the electric inter-city train, the author's opinion is that the new proposal is the best solution, with the conventional locomotive-hauled train second and SET third in the ranking.

Diesel inter-city trains

There should be a diminishing number of diesel inter-city trains as electrification is extended. Given the Government's commitment to work towards a low carbon economy, it would not make sense to retain diesel traction on the busier routes. Electric trains powered by renewable or nuclear energy sources are surely the best way forward for a national rail strategy compatible with national energy policy over the medium term. Even some of the less busy routes are natural candidates for electrification; for example the abundance of hydro electric power in the Scottish highlands, together with the twisting nature of the routes, would make electrification to Aberdeen and Inverness a logical choice when it can be afforded. Equally, the Cornish main line beyond Plymouth may benefit from neighbouring offshore wind farms, and the Bristol and Cardiff areas may take advantage from tidal power from the Severn.

It is assumed, therefore, that a comprehensive electrification programme will be authorised, in contrast to past opposition from the civil servants. Consequently, there will be few long diesel inter-city trains, and those few can be powered either by existing *Class 67* locomotives or ex-HST power cars in pairs. For an interim period, many such trains will operate over electrified routes for most of their journeys, so locomotives would be changed at the boundaries. Often loadings will be lower on the diesel sections of route, so train lengths can be reduced at the same time to give good performance and reasonable journey times with only single locomotives. This is in contrast to the hybrid SET, which is effectively a fixed formation train, so it will have low acceleration when operating under diesel power only, resulting in longer journey times.

The proposed train design strategy also has the advantage of avoiding investment in new diesel traction, which will have diminishing usefulness as electrification proceeds. The approach is also more energy-efficient than a conventional diesel locomotive-hauled train, with some energy recovery through regenerative braking and reduced brake wear. Consequently, it should have somewhat lower running costs than the conventional diesel-hauled train.

Cross country trains

Moving on to the longer secondary cross country routes, an incremental investment programme can be chosen as described earlier. This returns to the old idea that such routes can take advantage of the best second hand equipment displaced from the main lines, giving good performance and comfort at low cost. Each eight-plus-two HST inter-city train made redundant by electrification yields two four-coach cross country trains by the addition of two driving trailers (one for each train). These driving trailers, identical to those built for the inter-city trains, allow HST performance levels and top speeds of 125mph, improve fuel efficiency, give emergency power backup, provide basic self-service refreshment facilities at all times and have a large cycle storage space. The proposed train allows a dramatic improvement in comfort and performance from the typical *Class 158* or *Class 170* DMU which operates such services now, with top speeds of only 90 or 100mph.

To start with, this concept could use the four existing *Mk. 3* coaches in a fixed formation. In time, two new articulated coach triplets can replace them, introducing step-free access, eliminating slam doors, improving comfort with greater width and seat spacing, and giving the flexibility to alter train formations easily. Finally, when the ex-HST diesel power cars reach the end of their lives they are replaced by new diesel or electric locomotives. By that time, many routes might be electrified throughout or move to full inter-city status.

Both the driving trailers and coaches are identical to the inter-city designs, so they can easily be transferred between routes according to their success in attracting additional traffic. Many such trains operate in areas where few people are rail users due to traditionally poor services, so there is plenty of untapped potential to produce dramatic increases in loadings by providing much more attractive services. Some other routes are chronically overcrowded already and desperately need more capacity and performance; this incremental approach provides a way of meeting that demand without excessive capital expenditure.

For busier secondary routes that could be electrified early as 'add-ons' to the main line programme, a low cost interim solution might be the use of older electric locomotives instead of ex-HST power cars. This would allow fairly fast journey times with longer trains, although top speed would be limited to 110mph. In time, the locomotives could be replaced by the standard 150mph inter-city types. When finances are tight, it is probably better to spend the limited money on electrification and infrastructure improvements rather than new trains, making use of refurbished second hand rolling stock where practical.

The infrastructure works should be done to a good standard without skimping on materials, though; that would only lead to greater costs in the long term, as has been discovered often enough in the past. Upgraded routes should be made fit for robust 150mph operation where the topography permits, even if the trains cannot yet go at that speed, and power supplies should be sufficient for expanded traffic levels to avoid the need for expensive later upgrades. As the electric network expands, there are more opportunities for power supply strengthening and synergies by interconnecting several routes. Perhaps also this can tie in with the need to upgrade the national electricity grid to cope with all the new energy sources and home generation possibilities coming along in the next few years, contributing to a low carbon energy infrastructure in line with environmental policy.

Stopping trains

The re-equipment of the secondary cross country services as described above releases a number of better quality diesel multiple units for the improvement of local stopping services. In combination with the electrification of several local commuter services, this should reduce the demand for DMUs significantly and will allow the poorest ones (the Pacers) to head for the scrap yard where they belong. For shorter distance stopping services, therefore, there will not be a high demand for new trains in the medium term.

Something should be done about longer distance stopping services, though. A journey time of about two hours is long enough to have to endure the level of comfort of a DMU (even a good DMU like a *Class 170*), so the long-distance stopping services would get new trains with diesel power cars and low-density coach triplets as proposed in this strategy. Routes such as the Far North, West Highland, Heart of Wales, Settle and Carlisle, Cumbrian Coast, Lincolnshire, Birmingham to Aberystwyth, West Wales and Cornwall would be among the natural places for this approach.

In addition to rather faster journey times and much greater comfort that the new trains would provide, many of these routes are also candidates for trying the low-density sleeping car strategy described earlier, much improving the usefulness of the railway in these areas. The flexibility of the concept allows easy arrangement of through coaches from long-distance inter-city services too if required. These improvements should enhance the attractiveness of these scenic routes to casual tourists significantly, generating much better loadings at least in summer.

With the single engine hybrid drive philosophy there should be good fuel efficiency and low maintenance costs, and the introduction of overnight services and faster journeys might simplify maintenance regimes and/or give additional 'departmental' facilities for remote areas as described earlier.

In time, when the *Class 153, 156* and *158* DMUs are retired on shorter-distance services, the new stopping trains would replace them. The resulting improvements in comfort and speed should enhance traffic levels, and the new trains would give the possibility of introducing long-distance through coaches to more places.

Commuter trains

For the really heavy long-distance commuter flows (e.g. from London to Northampton / Birmingham, Corby / Leicester, King's Lynn, Ipswich etc.) the proposed solution uses the same 150mph locomotives and coaches as the inter-city train but with higher-density seating. This should provide attractive commuter services to shift the heavy loads, while minimising their disruptive impact on inter-city services sharing the same tracks. There is also the flexibility to swap identical locomotives and driving trailers between commuter and inter-city services as necessary. By upgrading these heavily used long-distance services, existing 100mph electric trains are released to enhance capacity on shorter-distance outer suburban commuter services.

The London schemes of Thameslink upgrade and Crossrail will dominate the situation for 'outer suburban' electric trains. The provision of new trains for Thameslink will release large numbers of the existing trains for use elsewhere, providing the opportunity to enhance commuter services around provincial cities using infill electrification schemes. As described before, in financially challenging times it would be better to invest in infrastructure and live with refurbished second hand trains in the meantime to make extensive electrification affordable.

So there is probably not a high demand for new outer suburban trains outside London in the shorter term. In the longer term, the solution described in this book is recommended, as it can give much better off-peak journey schedules and (with fewer motors and drives) should reduce maintenance costs. In addition, there is the flexibility (and potential cost savings) to swap coaches between commuter and other services.

As for the London schemes, a choice has to be made between a conventional EMU solution (with fixed power to weight ratio for each unit), and the mixed powered / unpowered unit philosophy advocated here. Given the intensive use of the inner city sections of route, rather special measures (such as automatic train control and platform doors) may be needed. The tight headways and high traffic densities encountered throughout the day may limit the scope for taking advantage of the flexibility of the proposed approach. Consequently, a conventional EMU philosophy may well be chosen as it is simpler to manage, and its limitations are not so significant under these operating circumstances. Some aspects of the proposed outer suburban solution would still be worthwhile, however: articulation for greater width and a lower floor for step-free access are very useful features under such conditions. With less need for flexibility in length, a greater degree of articulation could be considered to keep train weights down.

For Crossrail, it should be carefully considered whether a higher platform in the central tunnel sections is a good idea. This method of giving level access creates another platform height standard which is different to the current well-established one: in the author's opinion it would be better to lower train floors to give level access to all platforms, using the techniques described earlier. The approach can work equally well whether platform doors are fitted or not.

When the time comes to re-equip outer suburban commuter services outside the Thameslink and Crossrail service areas, the strategy described here with powered and unpowered coach triplets can give significant improvements in comfort and off-peak journey times, compared with the conventional EMUs they replace.

There are not many inner suburban commuter services using AC electrification: in Manchester, Newcastle, Sheffield, Nottingham, Edinburgh and elsewhere these functions are (or will be) performed mostly by metro or tram services. The main candidates for such trains will be Glasgow, Birmingham and Cardiff, plus a few routes in London; elsewhere the dominant services are more of an outer suburban character and that solution is probably preferable. Where inner suburban trains are really needed, the proposed solution can deliver faster off-peak journeys and potentially reduced maintenance costs through the combination of powered and unpowered coach quintuplets.

Overall synergies

Although the train design concept described may seem complex, there are many common components giving opportunities for cost savings through economies of scale.

There are only two designs of coach structure: lightweight quintuplets for inner suburban services and medium-weight triplets for all other coaches. Coach bodies may have windows fitted in different positions, giving great flexibility for any desired layout according to the requirements of individual operators.

Train controls are standardized. The train information bus is one standard protocol with flexibility to adapt to new facilities and vehicle types with minimum extra wiring. Information terminals for drivers and guards have a common design.

There are only two designs of unpowered bogie; one for the inner suburban train and the other for the rest. Few types of powered bogie are needed either: the local diesel stopping train and the electric outer suburban train use the same design. A further three designs cover the locomotive, driving trailer and inner suburban train requirements.

Much of the power equipment for the inner and outer suburban trains is identical too. All trains have the same couplers and corridor connections. The sliding access doors have one common single leaf design for most trains, plus one double leaf design for inner suburban trains.

Adopting a coordinated train design philosophy has benefits for the infrastructure as well. All coaches have a standard 14m spacing between bogies, and other vehicles have the same or a shorter spacing. This makes it relatively easy to have universal route availability: once it is decided what vehicle width and body profile can be permitted using such short designs, all vehicles conforming to this strategy can travel anywhere on the network. Apart from simplifying the logistics in times of disruption, excursion trains can be organised easily without reference to a time-consuming approval process for authorising particular trains to travel on particular routes.

The commonalities of design also have considerable benefits in terms of staff training, allowing them to become familiar with standard components and skilled and efficient at using and maintaining them. Spare part inventories can be simplified too, reducing the need to stock special items which might be seldom required. In case of incident, vehicles and components can be moved where needed rapidly, with no surprises for staff unfamiliar with different designs.

The complete range of vehicle types required for the proposed strategy is summarised in *Figure 33*.

A common 'one railway' technical strategy?

It is easy to advocate a common technical strategy for the British railway network from a theoretical point of view, but this does not fit well with the current organisational structure and regulatory regime. At present, two dozen train operating companies have mostly medium-term franchises (e.g. ten years) agreed with the civil servants on the basis of service levels and financial deals (subsidy or premium). Often train companies have little freedom to choose their rolling stock, but have to live with what happens to be available from their predecessors or dictated by officials. They may spend money on refurbishment, but with shorter contracts and much dynamic movement of franchises there is a risk that some of the rewards for improving standards by such investment may be harvested by other companies. This fragmentation of the industry and shorter-term focus without much expert engineering input in

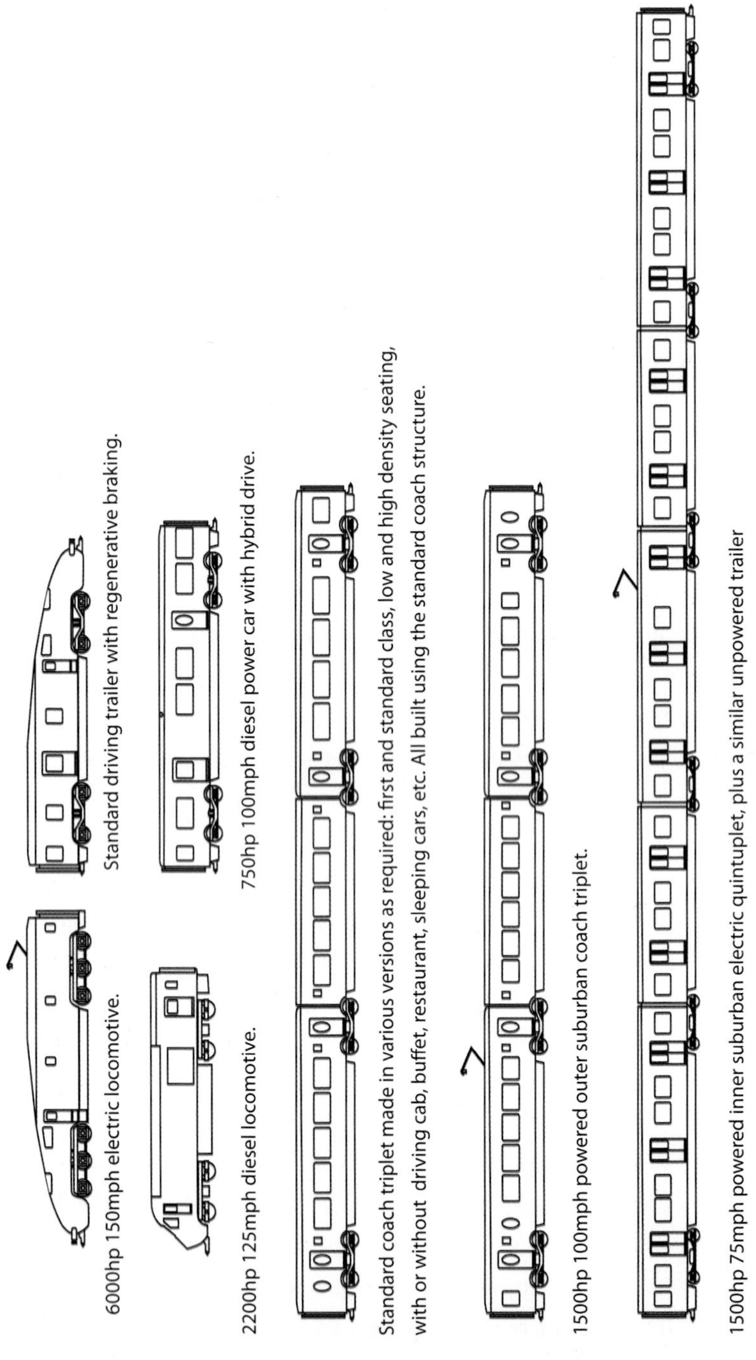
6000hp 150mph electric locomotive.
Standard driving trailer with regenerative braking.
2200hp 125mph diesel locomotive.
750hp 100mph diesel power car with hybrid drive.
Standard coach triplet made in various versions as required: first and standard class, low and high density seating,
with or without driving cab, buffet, restaurant, sleeping cars, etc. All built using the standard coach structure.
1500hp 100mph powered outer suburban coach triplet.
1500hp 75mph powered inner suburban electric quintuplet, plus a similar unpowered trailer

Figure 33: *Components of the train design strategy summarised. Only 8 different vehicle types are needed to cover the whole range of passenger trains from the highest capacity 150 mph long distance service to the smallest local stopping train.*

policy-making makes it difficult to arrange (or even to accept the need for) a coherent long-term nationwide technical strategy for the design of rolling stock.

The fact that the system does not facilitate the formulation of a consistent long-term technical strategy does not mean that it is unimportant, however. Suppose the present regime continues, some companies have more than one train operating franchise and none collaborate technically: the result could be about ten different requested rolling stock strategies, driven by the desire of each company to have its own distinctive policy in a competitive environment. If this were translated into real hardware it would gradually worsen an already serious problem of incompatibility between vehicles and restrictions on who could maintain them. The rolling stock leasing companies will influence a reduction in this diversity, though, being concerned to have assets with as wide an applicability as possible.

In practice, however, there is no real need for several rolling stock design strategies. While much is made of branding to emphasise the differences between train companies, and passengers are treated to lots of colourful liveries and different station signs every time a franchise changes, by and large a given route has the same staff with the same trains running on the same rails between the same stations to much the same timetable, with the same passengers travelling for the same purposes paying much the same (possibly regulated) fares. The technical requirements to satisfy those demands efficiently are actually much the same whoever is in charge, annoying though no doubt it is to say so as far as the train operating companies are concerned.

There is not much logic in making trains substantially less capable than the engineering constraints permit unless costs are dramatically reduced, and even then the loss of revenue through offering lower standards may offset any savings made. So an innovative engineering strategy which pushes train design to the achievable limits at a reasonable cost is probably in the best interests of all train companies, with little need for significant differences. Such differences as seating layout and décor can be accommodated easily within the strategy proposed to meet the brand image of the current franchisee. Practically speaking, the train operating company exercises its distinctiveness through the level of service provided and the efficiency with which it delivers that service, together with its branding and image. Unless the regime changes to allow much longer franchises, giving stability for a company to reap the rewards of its long-term investment, there is little real scope for a train company to determine its own special rolling stock strategy.

Since trains have a long lifetime, a useful criterion against which to evaluate any design strategy is the opinion of future railway managers as well as current ones. Of course, it is difficult to predict what they will think in twenty or forty years' time, but it can be confidently stated that the environment and regulatory regime will be different. Quite *how* it will be different is harder to say, so building in the maximum degree of flexibility possible is definitely a Good Thing. The proposed strategy certainly achieves great flexibility, as has been described; however it is not essential to use it. If a train operator only wants to run fixed formation trains all day, it is possible to do that with the proposed strategy just as easily as using a conventional approach. When the rolling stock moves to another operator, however, the flexibility is still there to change train formations in a more creative way if desired.

The same flexibility is also useful if the pendulum of fashion swings back to public rather than private ownership of the system. If a future British Peoples' Railway decides that as a matter of public policy and national cohesion a nightly sleeper service between Harlow Town and Harlech is essential, that can be arranged without any technical difficulty. On the other hand, if in a lightly regulated privatised environment the Buccaneering International Transportation Corporation thinks that the way to get a slice of the market is to offer a service between Hastings and Halifax via Haywards Heath, Heathrow, Heyford, Hinckley, Hucknall and Huddersfield, that can be done too. The flexibility of the design strategy advocated here is useful for both extremes of regulatory regimes (and for more sensible ones in the middle too).

Undoubtedly there are many obstacles to be overcome if this coherent nationwide strategy is to be adopted, but it is not necessary to have an 'all-or-nothing' strategic decision. For example, before the train information bus and couplers are designed, it would still be possible to build some coach triplets and try them out in fixed formations, replacing conventional coaches. Later, the new couplers and train information bus could be retro-fitted to give the desired flexibility.

Alternatively, some driving trailers could be built and tested out with 'half HSTs' using their existing coaches. This would prove the feasibility and cost-effectiveness of the proposed regenerative braking and battery storage concepts, before graduating to the more challenging full-length 150mph electric trains.

Another approach would be to build some diesel power cars and trailer triplets for long-distance stopping trains on scenic routes, to see if they had the desired effect of increasing tourist patronage. There are often grumbles about the use of 'suburban DMUs' on such routes, and the new trains should dramatically improve comfort. In the unlikely event of insufficient increases in patronage, the trains would be useful for lower capacity cross country services.

In all these ways, and no doubt many others too, it should be possible gradually to converge on a coordinated technical strategy through satisfying specific demands but bearing in mind the long-term strategic objectives. Of course it will be very many years before the strategy becomes universal, even if the industry embraces the ideas enthusiastically: but still, it should be possible to get there eventually!

In conclusion, the proposed train design strategy appears to offer many benefits over conventional approaches in terms of improved performance, comfort and flexibility, in a cost-effective way. Railway professionals are invited to assess the possibilities of this strategy for themselves.

It was an interesting and enjoyable exercise to put this proposal together. With all those opportunities to indulge in a bit of shunting, undoubtedly Thomas would approve of the strategy too!

Sources and further reading

- Ford, Roger. *Bi-mode defies rational analysis*. Informed Sources, *Modern Railways* magazine, May 2009.
- Ford, Roger. *Super Express – quick off the mark*. Informed Sources, *Modern Railways* magazine, April 2009.
- Johnston, Howard and Harris, Ken. *Jane's Train Recognition Guide*. HarperCollins Publishers, 2005.
- Marsden, Colin J. *The DC Electrics*. Oxford Publishing Co., 2008.
- Marsden, Colin J. *The Second Generation DMUs*. Oxford Publishing Co., 2009.
- Semmens, Peter. *Electrifying the East Coast Route: The making of Britain's first 140 mph railway*. Patrick Stephens Limited, 1991.
- Tian, Hong-qi. *Formation Mechanism of Aerodynamic Drag of High-Speed Train and Some Reduction Measures*. *Journal of Central South University Technology*, Vol.16, no.1, February 2009. Central South University, Changsha, China. http://www.springerlink.com/content/g181061nl3778534/
- Tufnell, R. M. *InterCity 125,* Super Profile. Haynes Publishing Group, 1984.
- Walmsley, Ian. *What we want from son of IEP. Modern Railways* magazine, February 2009. Also comments on the article (including 'Design issues' from the present author) in the Forum section of the March 2009 issue.

Index

(Page numbers in **BOLD** refer to illustrations)

U

V

W